Karl A. Roider

The World of Music

SONG PARADE

By

MABELLE GLENN

DIRECTOR OF MUSIC, PUBLIC SCHOOLS, KANSAS CITY, MISSOURI

HELEN S. LEAVITT

DIRECTOR OF MUSIC, THE WHEELOCK SCHOOL, BOSTON, MASSACHUSETTS
AND INSTRUCTOR IN MUSIC, BOSTON UNIVERSITY

VICTOR L. F. REBMANN

DIRECTOR, DEPARTMENT OF MUSIC, ITHACA COLLEGE, ITHACA, NEW YORK

GINN AND COMPANY

BOSTON · NEW YORK · CHICAGO · LONDON · ATLANTA · DALLAS · COLUMBUS · SAN FRANCISCO

The World of Music

KINDERGARTEN	GRADES I-VIII	ALL GRADES
SING A SONG	LISTEN AND SING	SINGING DAYS
PLAY A TUNE	TUNING UP	
	RHYTHMS AND RIMES	
	SONGS OF MANY LANDS	
	BLENDING VOICES	
	TUNES AND HARMONIES	
	SING ALONG	
	SONG PARADE	

ACKNOWLEDGMENTS

The editors wish to thank the group who by constructive suggestions have contributed to the artistic value of this book.

Acknowledgment is due also to Little, Brown & Company for permission to use the poem "Bingo, the Dingo, and the Fatal Flamingo," from *Tirra Lirra* by Laura E. Richards; to The Macmillan Company for permission to use "Roadways," from *Poems* by John Masefield; and to Mrs. Mildred Plew Meigs for permission to use her poem "Pirate Don Durk of Dowdee."

The Spanish melody on page 25 and the Polish melody on page 93 are reprinted from Folk Song Sight Singing Series, Book II and Book IV, by permission of the Oxford University Press, Carl Fischer, Inc., New York, sole agents in the United States of America. The Ukrainian melody on page 90 and the Russian melody on page 140 are used by arrangement with Henry Lefkowitch. "Wandering Cowboy" is reprinted from *Singing Cowboy* by Margaret Larkin, by permission of and special arrangement with Alfred A. Knopf, Inc., authorized publishers.

Classified Contents

TOPICS

3

Classified Contents

VOICE ARRANGEMENTS

ACCOMPANIMENTS

The songs on the following pages are provided with piano accompaniments:

MARGUERITE DAVIS.

SONG PARADE

Pirate Don Durk of Dowdee

9

black as a bat, But he had a flop-pet-y plume on his hat, And when he went walk-ing it jig-gled like that! The plume of the Pi-rate Dow-dee. · His coat it was crim-son and cut with a slash, And of-ten as ev-er he twirled his mus-tache, Deep down in the o-cean the

The Marines' Hymn[1]

L. Z. PHILLIPS

1. From the halls of Mon - te - zu - ma, To the shores of Trip-o - li, We fight our coun-try's bat - tles, On the land as on the sea. Ad-mi-

2. Our flag's un - furled to ev - 'ry breeze, From dawn to set-ting sun. We have fought in ev - 'ry clime and place, Where we could take a gun; In the

[1] Used by permission of Edward B. Marks Music Corporation, owner of the copyright.

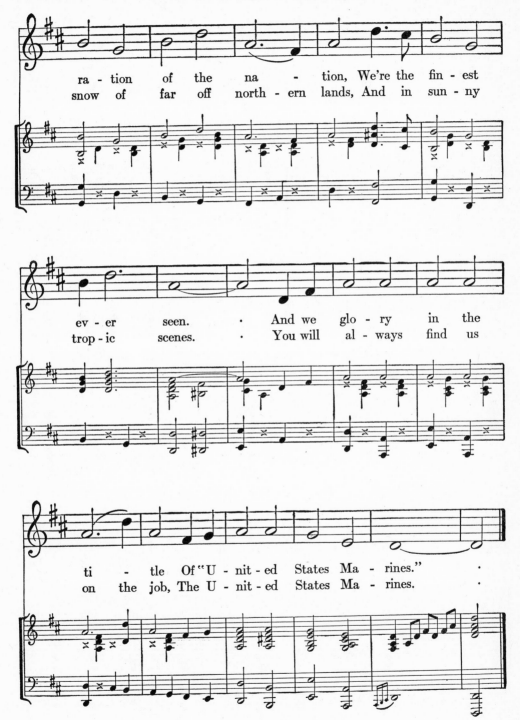

Northern Harvest

Translated by
CHRISTINE TURNER CURTIS

POLISH FOLK SONG

1. Coun - try - men, coun - try - men,
2. Coun - try - men, coun - try - men,

Lo, the har - vest fields are glow - ing; Au - tumn gath - ers
While the heav - y teams are wind - ing, Raise the har - vest

on the fen, Sum - mer days are go - ing.
song a - gain, Ev - 'ry heart re - mind - ing

Parts optional[1]

Clouds a - bove the plain are fly - ing, High and low are
Thanks are due to God, the giv - er; Un - to Him be

Clouds a - bove the plain are fly - ing, High and low are
Thanks are due to God, the giv - er; Un - to Him be

voic - es ring - ing. Down the wheat-fields, down the rye - fields,
praise for - ev - er. Down the wheat-fields, down the rye - fields,

voic - es ring - ing. Down the wheat - fields, down the rye - fields,
praise for - ev - er. Down the wheat - fields, down the rye - fields,

[1] In the part arrangement the bass is confined to two notes, 1 and 5, and therefore is very easy.

Adapted from the original

1. Once in a
2. "The ver - y

blithe green - wood Lived a her - mit wise and good, Whom the
long - est lane Has a turn - ing it is plain, And the

folks from far and near For his coun - sel sought, Know-ing
dark - est clouds will fly; And what can't be cured Must with

well that what he taught The drear - i - est of hearts would
pa - tience be en - dured. As cheap - ly can we laugh as

cheer. Though his hair was white His eye was clear and bright, And he
cry." If an ear you'll lend You'll hear that cheer - y friend Like the

thus was ev - er wont to say, "Though to care we are born, Yet the
voice of hope when skies are gray, "Though to care we are born, Yet the

The Hermit (*Continued*)

dull - est morn Of - ten her - alds in the fair - est
dull - est morn Of - ten her - alds in the fair - est

day! Though to care we are born, Yet the
day! Though to care we are born, Yet the

dull - est morn Of - ten her - alds in the fair - est day. "
dull - est morn Of - ten her - alds in the fair - est day. "

Pretty Polly Oliver

TRADITIONAL

ENGLISH FOLK SONG

Allegro moderato

1. As pret-ty Pol-ly Ol-i-ver sat mus-ing, 'tis said, A com-i-cal fan-cy came in-to her head; No fa-ther nor moth-er shall make me false prove, I'll list for a sol-dier and fol-low my love.

2. So in sol-dier's at-tire to the wars she set out, And bore a brave part in both raid and in rout; In bat-tle she found him slight-ly wound-ed and low, On the ground where he lay with his face to the foe.

3. The ser-geant he sent for the par-son to come, And cou-ple the lov-ers who'd fol-lowed the drum, And Pol-ly re-stored to her wom-an-ly state Found all she had sought in a home and a mate.

The Flag Goes By

Henry Holcomb Bennett

C. E. Connew

Hats off! Hats off! The flag is pass - ing

by! · A - long the crowd-ed street there comes A blare of trum-pets, a

ruf - fle of drums, A flash of col - or be - neath the sky: The

flag   is   pass-ing   by!   ·   Blue and crim-son and white it shines

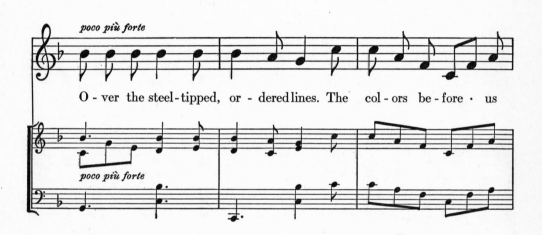

O - ver the steel-tipped, or - dered lines. The   col - ors be - fore · us

fly;   ·   But more than the flag · goes by,   ·   Sign   of a na - tion

strong,   Guard-ing us from wrong;   Pride and glo - ry,

hon - or, all   Live in the col-ors to stand or fall.   Hats   off!

Hats off! The flag is pass - ing by!   A - long the crowd-ed

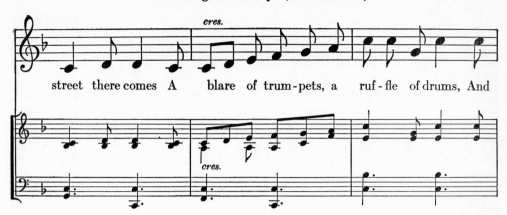

street there comes A blare of trum-pets, a ruf-fle of drums, And

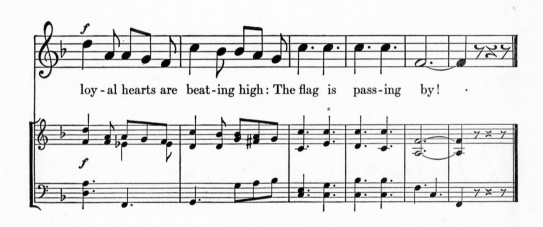

loy-al hearts are beat-ing high: The flag is pass-ing by!

Mariquita

Adapted from the Spanish by
HANNAH BAILEY

SPANISH FOLK SONG

UNISON

1. Mar-i-qui-ta, Mar-i-
2. Mar-i-qui-ta, Mar-i-

Second part optional

qui - ta,   For the glim-mer   of a smile,   · On my po - ny,
qui - ta,   I will bring you   jew - els rare,   · Gems to bright-en,

lean and bo - ny,   I would gal - lop   man-y a mile.   Like a
and to light-en,   In the dark-ness   of your hair,   And a

swal-low,   o - ver hol-low,   O-ver plain I · would ride,   · I'd
ban - gle,   made to dan-gle,   Like a star bright and clear.   · I'll

stray not,   I'd de - lay not,   Till I came   to your side.   ·
please you,   and ap-pease you,   With a pearl   for your ear.   ·

Green Trees

JOHAN KROHN
Translated

EDVARD GRIEG

1. Green trees, green trees with your no - ble boughs, You cast a shade in the noon - tide burn-ing. In your tall branch-es the song - birds house, Lulled all night long by a leaf - y churn-ing. In shad - ows hold us, green trees, and fold us In qui - et dreams.

2. Green trees, green trees, when the south wind sighs, A mi - nor tune in your boughs goes hum-ming, Made up of mur-mur-ing lull - a - bies Like vi - o - lins in a leaf - y strum-ming. With shad - ows calm us, green trees, and charm us To peace - ful sleep.

Arise, Ye Sons and Daughters

English version by
JOHN SUMNER

WOLFGANG AMADEUS MOZART

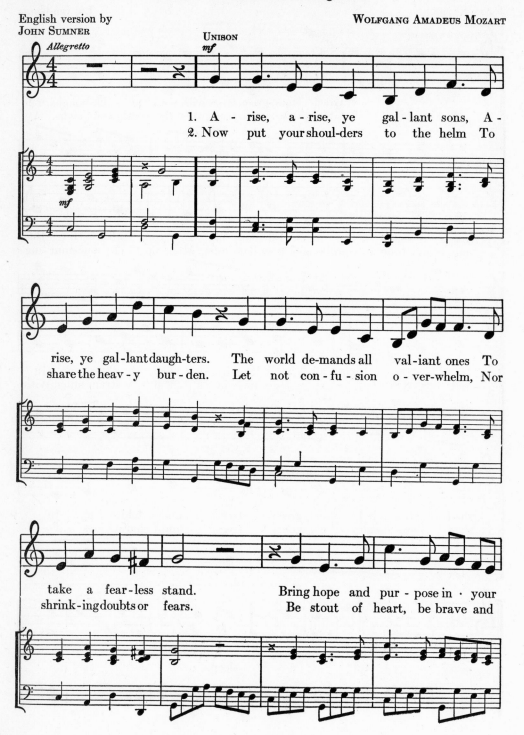

1. A - rise, a - rise, ye gal - lant sons, A -
2. Now put your shoul-ders to the helm To

rise, ye gal-lant daugh-ters. The world de-mands all val-iant ones To
share the heav - y bur - den. Let not con - fu - sion o - ver-whelm, Nor

take a fear-less stand. Bring hope and pur - pose in · your
shrink-ing doubts or fears. Be stout of heart, be brave and

hearts, And cour - age high that youth im - parts. A - rise,
strong, For right is might, and truth is · long. A - rise,

· ye sons and daugh - ters, A - rise · and lend a help - ing · hand.
· ye sons and daugh - ters, A - rise · and lend a help - ing · hand.

Give Us a Song

CHRISTINE TURNER CURTIS

LILY STRICKLAND

1. Day by day and year by year 'tis
2. Trou - bles have no pow'r a - gainst us

good · to be to-geth - er, Meet - ing hopes and
while · we are to-geth - er, Joy a - bounds when

fac - ing fears through storm and · sun; Shar - ing ev - 'ry
we are work - ing side by · side. Be our prog-ress

sport and game, press - ing for - ward in - to fame,
fast or slow, ev - 'ry year we wis - er grow;

molto cres.

Guard - ing well our coun-try's name, faith - ful ev - 'ry one.
Ev - 'ry wrong we o - ver-throw fills our hearts with pride.

School friends to-geth-er, staunch and true, Come, give us a song.

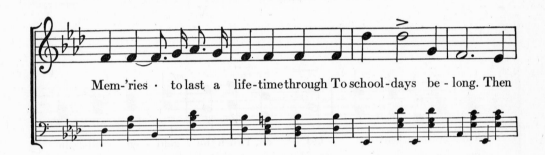

Mem-'ries · to last a life-time through To school-days be - long. Then

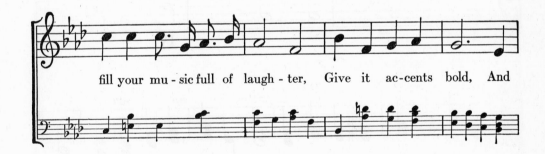

fill your mu - sic full of laugh - ter, Give it ac-cents bold, And

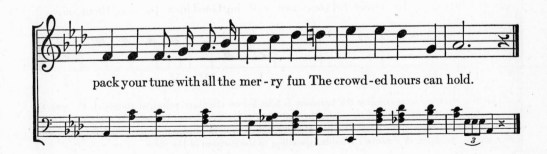

pack your tune with all the mer - ry fun The crowd-ed hours can hold.

Fisher Folk[1]

English version by
FRANCES FORD

FINNISH FOLK SONG

1. At the set of sun from the ros - y foam Come the
2. In their boats a - gain in the chill - y dawn, Sail the

I   V

fish - er-men, heav - y lad - en. Down the gold - en sands, in
men for the deep - sea trawl - ing. And their wives once more from

I   IV

smil-ing bands, Stroll wife and child and maid-en To wel-come sail - ors home.
cot-tage door, In cheer-ful tones are call-ing Good luck to speed them on.

I   IV   V   I   IV V   I

[1] This is a chording song because the harmony is founded on the three principal chords, I, IV, and V. As the root of I is the first tone of the scale, the root of IV is the fourth tone of the scale, and the root of V is the fifth tone of the scale, the bass is limited to three scale tones. In singing their part the basses may sing scale syllables, numbers, or a neutral syllable, according to the decision of the class.

Weave Her a Garland

GOETHE
Translated

LUDWIG VAN BEETHOVEN

1. Fair one, I'll plait a wreath of crim - son ros - es,
2. Strong - er and clos - er than the wreath is plait - ed,

Wind green leaves that ev - 'ry bush un - clos - es.
Twine our hearts in faith and love re - lat - ed,

Shines the sun, your youth and grace il - lum - ing.
Twine our lives in con - stan - cy as - sur - ing;

You are like a rose in beau - ty bloom - ing.
Day by day they forge a chain en - dur - ing.

Aloha Oe[1]

Paraphrase from the original by
IDA M. BUNTING

QUEEN LILIUOKALANI

Espressivo
p

1. Soft the cloud that veils the moun-tain's height, The
2. Ev-'ry flow'r re-minds me of thy face, Though
3. What though part-ing bring a sud-den tear, Sweet

west-ern wind now fills our sail, And a song is borne a-cross the
fair-er than the flow'rs thou art; Ev-'ry dew-drop spar-kles with a
thoughts of thee will cheer my way. Friend-ly trust will ban-ish ev-'ry

night, Breath-ing mem-'ries of love which can-not fail.
trace Of the light thou hast shed up-on my heart.
fear, Friend-ly light lead me back to thee some day.

CHORUS

"Fare-well to thee, fare-well to thee," The

[1] Chording song.

brood - ing hills give back the sad re - frain; "May Heav - en guard and

keep our love so true, Un - til we meet a - gain."

How Lovely Are the Messengers

From the BIBLE

FELIX MENDELSSOHN

Andante con moto

How love - ly are the mes - sen - gers that bring us the gos - pel of

peace; How love - ly are the mes-sen-gers that bring us the gos-pel of peace.

Greenwood Days[1]

JOHN SUMNER
Andante

CHRISTOPHER WILLIBALD GLUCK

1. Oh, youth is a pag-eant of fresh morn-ing
2. The world shone with sun-light, no sky kept its

1. Youth is a pag-eant morn-ing
2. So bright the sun-light, no sky

days that glow. They gleam for-ev-er in rain-bow-col-ored
gloom and gray. No grief, no cold-ness be-dimmed the gold-en

days That gleam in rain-bow-col-ored
gray. No grief, no cold-ness dimmed the

cres.   *mf*

haze. When down through the green-wood we strolled, free from
day, For each was a he-ro of worlds wild and

haze. When in the wood we're free from
day, Each one a he-ro, worlds quite

care, Bright flow'rs in our hat-bands and spir-its light as air.
strange, Nor would we for king-doms our joy-ous lot ex-change.

care, With flow'rs and spir-its light as air.
strange, Nor would our joy-ous lot ex-change.

[1] Chording song.

Blue Bells of Scotland[1]

SCOTCH FOLK SONG

1. Oh, where, tell me where is your High-land lad-die gone? Oh,
2. Oh, where, tell me where did your High-land lad-die dwell? Oh,
3. Oh, what, tell me what if your High-land lad be slain? Oh,

where, tell me where is your High-land lad-die gone? He's
where, tell me where did your High-land lad-die dwell? He
what, tell me what if your High-land lad be slain? Oh

gone with stream-ing ban - ners where · no - ble deeds are
dwelt in bon - nie Scot - land where · blooms the sweet blue
no! True love will be his guard and · bring him safe a -

done, And it's oh, · in my heart, I · · wish him safe at home.
bell, And it's oh, · in my heart, I · · lo'e my lad-die well.
gain, For it's oh, my heart would break if my · High-land lad were slain.

[1] Chording song.

The American Flag

A. S. KENDALL

UNISON TRADITIONAL MELODY

1. Wave the stars and stripes be -
2. Wave the stars and stripes be -

fore you, Fair-est flag · on land or sea; · In its stars we read our
fore you, 'Tis the ban - ner of · the free; · And we love to tell the

glo - ry, In · its stripes our ear - ly sto - ry. Long
sto - ry Of · the flag we call Old Glo - ry. Long

wave the stars and stripes tri - um-phant, Flag of the brave and free.
wave the stars and stripes tri - um-phant, Flag of the brave and free.

Paraphrase by
ALICE M. CAHILL

WELSH FOLK SONG

1. Sing proud-ly, ye harps, in Mo-na's fair isle, Sing of
2. Sing sad-ly, ye harps, of storm on the deep, Of a

sail-ors, sing of war-riors by the cold north-ern sea Who
maid-en, of her sweet-heart who was lost on the main, Tide

hun-dreds of years bat-tled stout with the foe, To de-
in and tide out, lin-gered she by that shore Ev-er

fend their pre-cious is-land, to pre-serve it strong and free.
lov-ing, ev-er faith-ful, but she wait-ed all in vain.

In the Foggy Morning

PIERSON UNDERWOOD

LAWRENCE PERRY

1. Up the moun-tain, far and ear - ly,
2. Up the moun-tain, late or ear - ly,
3. Up the moun-tain, no use talk-ing,

Where the moun-tain mist is curl - y, There's a tune the
Where the moun-tain mist is curl - y, Moon - light sel - dom
Round a - bout as I've been walk-ing, I've heard things you'd

fid - dlers play: "In the Fog - gy Morn - ing." There you'll hear the
shines by day, In the fog - gy morn - ing! Woods are lone-some
nev - er know, In the fog - gy morn - ing! Girls in Tex - as

ban - jos plunk-ing, Birds a - whis - tling, bull - frogs chunk-ing,
in Ken - tuck - y; Take the right road, you'll be luck - y;
dress in sat - in, Girls in Maine speak Greek and Lat - in:

Far and faint at break of day, In the fog-gy morn - ing.
Take the wrong road, you'll get lost, In the fog-gy morn - ing.
I've heard tell these things are so, In the fog-gy morn - ing.

"Bow, bow! One, two, three, There's a girl that waits for me.
"'Way, 'way! Fid - dles play, Faint and sweet and far a - way.
"Low, low! One, two, three, Can't you stop to dance with me?

Oh, oh! Don't say no,   In the fog-gy morn - ing!" Up the moun-tain,
Oh, oh! Don't you go,   In the fog-gy morn - ing!" Up the moun-tain,
Oh, oh! Don't say no,   In the fog-gy morn - ing!" Ran de ri do,

bright and ear - ly, Where the mist is white and curl - y,
crisp and ear - ly, Thin the drift - ing mist, and curl - y,
I'll wed ear - ly, With a girl whose hair is curl - y;

That's the tune the fid - dlers play, In the fog - gy morn - ing.
While their tune the fid - dlers play, In the fog - gy morn - ing.
That's the tune the fid - dlers play, In the fog - gy morn - ing.

A Chilly Welcome

English version by
HANNAH BAILEY

CZECH FOLK SONG
Arranged by LAWRENCE PERRY

1. Knock a-gain, knock a-gain, Tap up-on the win-dow-pane.
2. Who is there? Who is there? Sau-cy youth or maid-en fair?

Stamp the ground, rap and pound, You will nev-er hear a sound.
Young or old, shy or bold, Your re-cep-tion will be cold.

Now my moth-er plucks a goose, Now my fa-ther ties a noose.
Is it com-mon sense you lack? Go a-way and don't come back.

Knock a-gain, knock a-gain, You will al-ways knock in vain.
Who is there? Who is there? Not a whit we know or care.

Iceland

Translated by
HANNAH BAILEY

NORWEGIAN FOLK SONG
Arranged by FREDERICK A. TAYLOR

1. Deep in the heart of the cold and froz - en north, Tales of the bleak long a - go Tell how an is - land lay be-neath the moon

2. Brave were the men who ad - ven - tured to the north, Wild as the sea - birds and bold; Out of the fjords they plied the lust - y oar,

3. Far in the north our fa - thers lit their fires, Head - lands and har - bors a - long. O - ver the cliffs and un - der-neath the moon

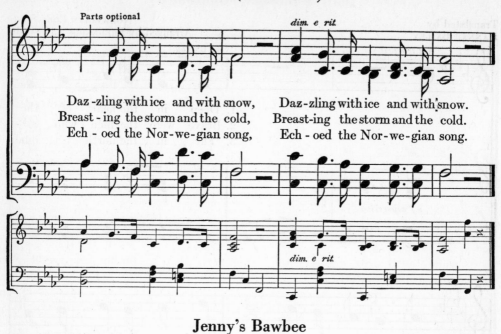

Parts optional

dim. e rit

Daz-zling with ice and with snow,   Daz-zling with ice and with snow.
Breast-ing the storm and the cold,   Breast-ing the storm and the cold.
Ech-oed the Nor-we-gian song,   Ech-oed the Nor-we-gian song.

dim. e rit

Jenny's Bawbee

Adapted from the original

Scotch Folk Song
Arranged by Phyllis Brown Freeman

Giocoso
mf

1. I · met four chaps a - mong the trees With
2. The · first, a cap - tain to his trade, Marched
3. She · bade the laird take off his wig, The
4. Then · John - ny came, a lad of sense. Al -

hang - ing ears and knock - ing knees. To · Neigh - bor Strong, I
round in red and gild - ed braid. A · law - yer brought his
sol - dier not to strut so big, The · law - yer not to
though he had not man - y pence This · youth was full of

cried, "Say, please, Who may they be?" Quoth he, "Those fel-lows
wag-ging tongue And pow'r-ful lung. A Scot-tish laird came
be a prig. "Tee-hee, tee-hee," The sim-ple fel-low
con-fi-dence. "Walk in," said she. Now John-ny pressed his

white as veal Came here to make a cun-ning deal, To
on a trip With spot-ted horse and sil-ver whip, A
told his tale; He knew that he could nev-er fail. She
suit so well Her heart grew soft be-neath the spell. He'll

win a love-ly maid and steal Our Jen-ny's baw-bee."
fool-ish fel-low longed to grip Our Jen-ny's baw-bee.
drenched him with the wa-ter pail, And kept her baw-bee.
have his share, we can fore-tell, In Jen-ny's baw-bee.

Dance in the Valley

MARTHA BANNING THOMAS

POLISH FOLK TUNE

Leggiero
mp

1. Flutes are play-ing, fid-dlers sway-ing, Tread the good earth kind-ly;
2. Quick-ly, Van-da, stamp your slip-per, Set your rib-bons swing-ing,

Dance in the Valley (*Continued*)

Stamp-ing, whirl-ing, bow-ing, twirl-ing, Let no sor-row
Smil-ing blithe-ly, bend-ing lithe-ly To the pol-kas

bind thee! Dance a-long the grass-y val-ley
ring-ing. See the trees and hills go rush-ing,

Where the sheep are · graz-ing. In the leaf-y
See the fields go · spin-ning. Nev-er grass or

shad-ows dal-ly While the gay ma-zur-kas sound.
pop-py crush-ing, Ev-er light and light-er bound.

The Hero Comes

English version by
JOHN SUMNER

FRENCH FOLK SONG

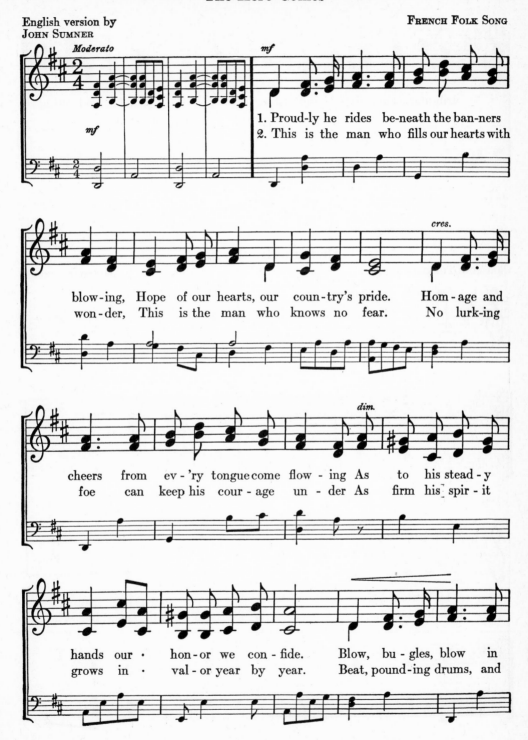

Moderato   mf   mf

1. Proud-ly he rides be-neath the ban-ners
2. This is the man who fills our hearts with

cres.

blow-ing, Hope of our hearts, our coun-try's pride. Hom-age and
won-der, This is the man who knows no fear. No lurk-ing

dim.

cheers from ev-'ry tongue come flow-ing As to his stead-y
foe can keep his cour-age un-der As firm his spir-it

hands our honor we con-fide. Blow, bu-gles, blow in
grows in val-or year by year. Beat, pound-ing drums, and

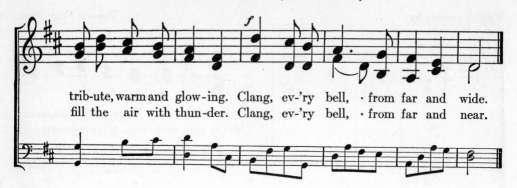

trib-ute, warm and glow-ing. Clang, ev-'ry bell, · from far and wide.
fill the air with thun-der. Clang, ev-'ry bell, · from far and near.

Dialogue by the Sea

CHRISTINE TURNER CURTIS   HARRY ELDRIDGE

1. As I was walk-ing
2. His boat lay on the

by the sea, Tra la la la la, the spar-kling sea, A
beach near by, Tra la la la la, 'twas quite near by. The

beard-ed   sail-or   called to __ me,   Tra la la la la, "A-
wa-ter   filled it   two feet high.   Tra la la la la, "No

SOPRANO and ALTO

mp

hoy!" said   he. "The   sun is bright; no ·   breez-es   stir, The
thanks," said   I. "I   ques-tion if your   boat will trim, And

ver - y   rip-ples ·   seem to   purr. What   say we   take   a
since I   neith-er ·   float nor   swim, My   chanc-es   look   a

BARITONE

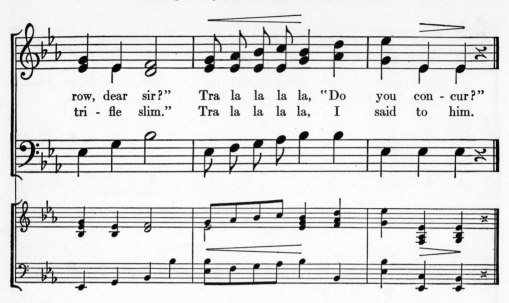

row, dear sir?"   Tra la la la la, "Do   you con - cur?"
tri - fle slim."   Tra la la la la, I   said to him.

Stand by the Flag

HENRY TUCKER

Maestoso e marcato
f UNISON

1. Stand   by   the flag;   its   folds have waved in glo - ry, To
2. Stand   by   the flag; though death-shots round it rat - tle, And

foes a fear, to friends a guard-ian robe, · And spread to na - tions
un - der-neath its wav - ing folds have met In all the dread ar -

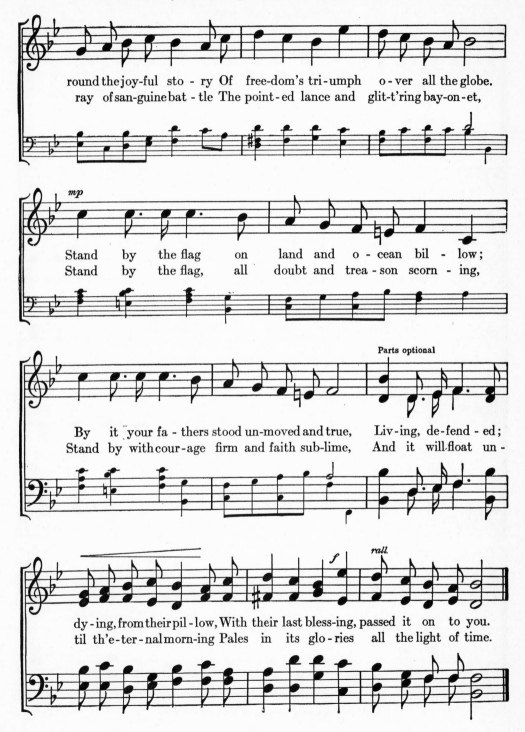

She'll Be Comin' Round the Mountain[1]

RECREATION SONG

TRADITIONAL   **TRADITIONAL**

1. She'll be com-in' round the moun-tain, When she comes.
2. Oh, we'll all · go to meet her, When she comes.

She'll be com-in' round the moun-tain, When she comes. She'll be
Oh, we'll all · go to meet her, When she comes. We will

com-in' round the moun-tain, She'll be com-in' round the
kill the old red roost-er, We will kill the old red

moun-tain, She'll be com-in' round · the moun-tain, When she comes. ·
roost-er, And we'll all have chick-en and dump-lin', When she comes. ·

[1] This song may be sung in unison if desired.

Adapted from the original

COWBOY SONG

1. We were ly - ing on the
2. Then up spoke a hand-some

prai - rie on a cold, win - ter night. Our heads were on our
cow - boy, with a look full of care, "My Kan - sas home is

sad - dles and our fires were burn-ing bright. And some were tell - ing
dear to me; I'm long - ing to be there; But, oh, I quar-reled

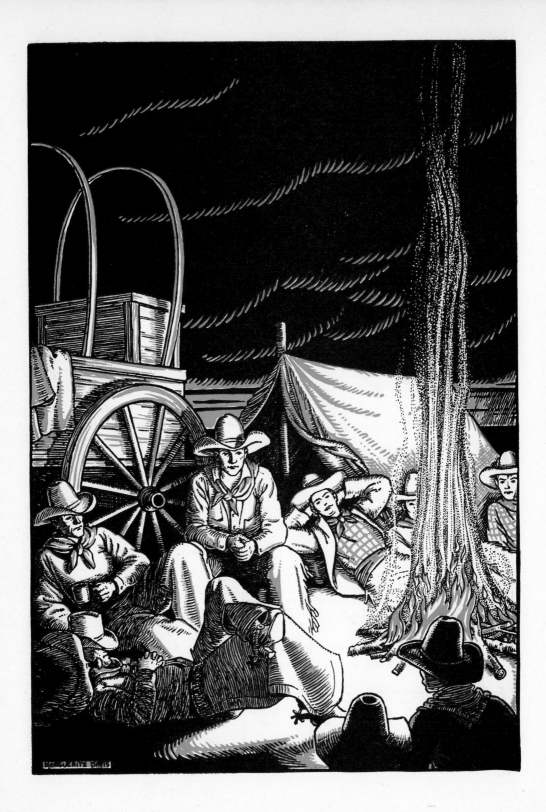

sto - ries while some   raised a   rous - ing   song,   And
with   a   friend; I   caused him   grief and   pain,   And

rall. e dim.

some were i - dly   dream-ing as the   dark hours rolled a - long.
now,   a - las, I'll   nev - er   see my   boy-hood home a - gain."

rall. e dim.

CHORUS[1]
a tempo
mp   *cres.*

It's a   low and paint-ed   cot - tage and   far a-way I   roam.   I'd

mp a tempo   *cres.*

8   ¹ Parts optional.

Wandering Cowboy (*Continued*)

give my po-ny and sad - dle to be at home, sweet home.

The Spanish Cavalier

RECREATION SONG

WILLIAM D. HENDRICKSON   WILLIAM D. HENDRICKSON

Cantabile
mp UNISON

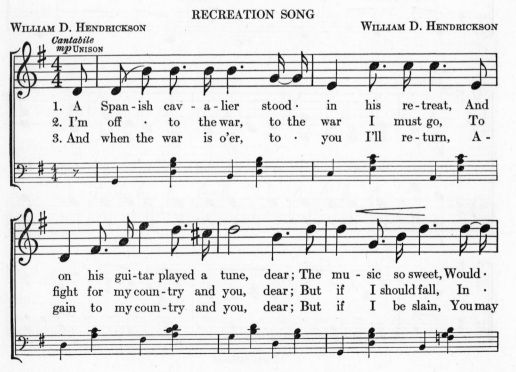

1. A Span-ish cav - a-lier stood · in his re-treat, And
2. I'm off · to the war, to the war I must go, To
3. And when the war is o'er, to · you I'll re-turn, A-

on his gui-tar played a tune, dear; The mu - sic so sweet, Would·
fight for my coun-try and you, dear; But if I should fall, In ·
gain to my coun-try and you, dear; But if I be slain, You may

oft - times re - peat The bless-ing of my coun - try and you, dear.
vain I would call, The bless-ing of my coun - try and you, dear.
seek me in vain, Up - on the bat-tle-field you will find me.

CHORUS[1]

Say, dar-ling, say, when I'm far a-way, Some-times you may think of

me, dear; Bright sun - ny days will soon fade a-way, Re-

mem - ber what I say, · and be true, dear.

[1] Parts are optional.

Prayer

Translated

CARL MARIA VON WEBER

1. Day is go - ing, Shad - ows · grow - ing,
2. Fa - ther, heed us, Fa - ther, · lead us,

Hearts in pray'r to God out - flow - ing;
With Thy Bread of Life oh, · feed · · · us;

Star - light · splen - dor, Faith - ful · and · ten - der,
So · to - mor - row, Kept from · all · sor - row,

Shows · in an - sw'ring beau - ty · ev - 'ry - where.
Shall · be joy - ful · through Thy · love and · care.

Translated

HUNGARIAN FOLK SONG

[1] Chording song. Tenor can be sung by unchanged voices as it has a range of 4 notes around middle C.

Wearing a Black Mantilla

John Sumner

Mexican Folk Tune

Grazioso
mp

1. Wear-ing a black man-til-la, · Perched on a pil-lion[1] high, ·
2. Maid on your Pa-lo-mi-no, · Rid-ing a-loof and high, ·

1. Black man-til-la, Perched on pil-lion high,
2. Pa-lo-mi-no, Rid-ing proud and high,

Fair Mar-gue-ri-ta, my se-ño-ri-ta, Can-ters se-rene-ly
How you a-larm me, oh, how you charm me, As you go rac-ing

Mar-gue-ri-ta Can-ters
You a-larm me, Rac-ing

by. Rid-ing a Pa-lo-mi-no,[2] · Shak-ing his cream-y
by. Rein in your Pa-lo-mi-no, · Tell him to graze a-

by. Pa-lo-mi-no Shakes his
by. Pa-lo-mi-no, Tell him

mane, · Show-ing his pac-es, air-ing her grac-es,
while, · O Mar-gue-ri-ta, my se-ño-ri-ta,

cream-y mane, Show-ing grac-es
graze a-while. Mar-gue-ri-ta,

[1] A kind of light saddle.   [2] A cream-colored pony.

Gal - lop - ing down the lane. Her bri - dle is set with
Give me a charm - ing smile. To look on your youth and

Down the lane. Her bri - dle is set with
Give a smile. To look on your youth and

sil - ver, · Her sad - dle of fin - est grain, · Gloss - y and sleek her
beau - ty, · I've trav-eled for man - y a mile, · Lean from your loft - y

po - ny Gal - lop-ing down the lane, Show-ing his pac - es,
pil - lion, Give me a charm-ing smile. O Mar-gue - ri - ta,

air - ing her grac - es, Gal - lop - ing down the lane. ·
my se - ño - ri - ta, Give me a charm - ing smile. ·

The Tailor and the Mouse

Adapted from the original by
FRANCES FORD

ENGLISH FOLK SONG

1. There was a tai-lor had a mouse; Hi did-dle un-kum
2. One day the mouse turned ver-y pale; Hi did-dle un-kum
3. The mous-e's face turned ver-y red; Hi did-dle un-kum

fee - dle. He kept him in the chick - en house.
fee - dle. The tai - lor gave him gin - ger ale.
fee - dle. "Please make it gin - ger tea!" he said.

1, 2, 3. Hi did-dle un-kum, fee - dle. Hi did - dle un-kum,

ta-rum, tan-tum, 'Through the town of Ram-say; Hi did-dle un-kum,

o - ver the lea, · Hi did - dle un - kum fee - dle.

Hark to the Drum[1]

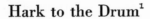

ADELBERT VON CHAMISSO
Translated and adapted

FRIEDRICH SILCHER
Arranged by MARJORIE BROOKS

1. Oh, hark how the rous - ing drum - beat · rolls, As rank aft - er rank pass
2. They march in - to man - hood, in - to · life, They march in - to years of

our pa - trols, So brave and proud in the glow - ing · sun. May
stress and · strife; And when the work of the day · is · done, May

God give them cour - age ev - 'ry - one, May God give them cour - age, ev - 'ry - one.
God give them glad - ness, ev - 'ry - one, May God give them glad - ness, ev - 'ry - one.

[1] This song is complete without the tenor part.

To God on High

Thomas H. Gill

Plainsong, 1539
Harmonized by Mendelssohn

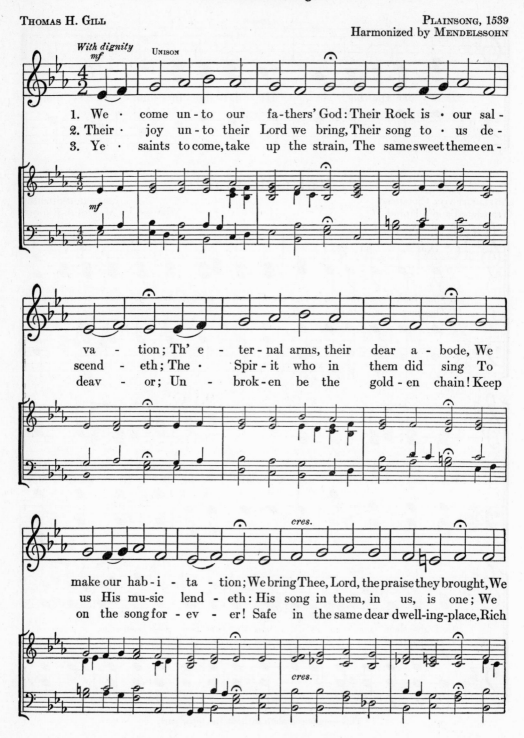

1. We · come un-to our fa-thers' God: Their Rock is · our sal-
2. Their · joy un-to their Lord we bring, Their song to · us de-
3. Ye · saints to come, take up the strain, The same sweet theme en-

va - tion; Th' e - ter-nal arms, their dear a - bode, We
scend - eth; The · Spir-it who in them did sing To
deav - or; Un - brok-en be the gold - en chain! Keep

make our hab-i - ta - tion; We bring Thee, Lord, the praise they brought, We
us His mu-sic lend - eth: His song in them, in us, is one; We
on the song for - ev - er! Safe in the same dear dwell-ing-place, Rich

seek Thee as Thy saints have sought In ev-'ry gen - er - a - tion.
raise it high, we send it on, The song that nev - er end - eth.
with the same e - ter-nal grace, Bless the same bound-less Giv - er.

Come, Thou Almighty King[1]

CHARLES WESLEY

FELICE DE GIARDINI

Maestoso

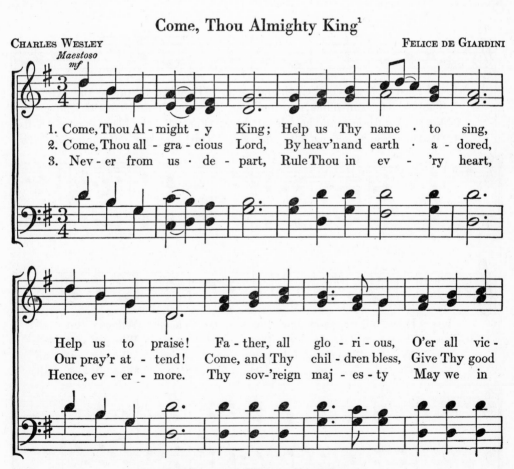

1. Come, Thou Al - might - y King; Help us Thy name · to sing,
2. Come, Thou all - gra - cious Lord, By heav'n and earth · a - dored,
3. Nev - er from us · de - part, Rule Thou in ev - 'ry heart,

Help us to praise! Fa - ther, all glo - ri - ous, O'er all vic -
Our pray'r at - tend! Come, and Thy chil - dren bless, Give Thy good
Hence, ev - er - more. Thy sov-'reign maj - es - ty May we in

[1] This song may be sung in unison if desired.

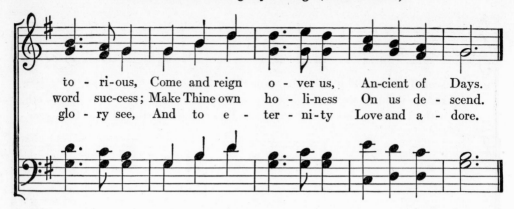

to - ri-ous, Come and reign o - ver us, An-cient of Days.
word suc-cess; Make Thine own ho - li-ness On us de - scend.
glo - ry see, And to e - ter-ni-ty Love and a - dore.

O Lord of Heaven

CHRISTOPHER WORDSWORTH

JOHN B. DYKES

Largo f UNISON

1. O Lord of heav'n and earth and sea, To Thee all praise and glo - ry
2. The gold-en sun-shine, ver - nal air, Sweet flow'rs and fruit, Thy love de -
3. For peace-ful homes and health-ful days, For all the bless-ings earth dis -
4. To Thee, from Whom we all de - rive Our life, our gifts, our pow'r to

be; How shall we show our love · to Thee, Who giv - est all?
clare; Where har-vests rip - en, Thou · art there, Who giv - est all.
plays, We owe Thee thank-ful - ness · and praise, Who giv - est all.
give; Oh, may we ev - er with · Thee live, Who giv - est all.

Softly, Softly Falls the Night

PIERSON UNDERWOOD

DANISH FOLK TUNE

1. Soft - ly, soft - ly falls the night. Stars, like can - dles,
2. Soft - ly, soft - ly goes the night; Till the stars, like

faint and spar - kling, Lift their twin - kling ta - per
can - dles shak - en, Quench in gold their fad - ing

light O - ver mead - ow and wood - land dark - 'ning.
light And the woods and the mead - ows wak - en.

The Maid by the River

Paraphrased from the original

WELSH FOLK SONG

sil - ver bells of · sweet - est tone While she her · sim - ple
laid her hand up - on my head; "These dole - ful · sighs you

sil - ver bells of sweet - est tone While she her · sim - ple
laid her hand up - on my head; "These dole - ful · sighs you

bal - lad · sang. My · heart beat hard and fast, I own. I
must re - strain, I · leave you not for long," she said. "One

bal - lad sang. My heart beat hard and fast, I own. I
must re - strain, I leave you not for long," she said. "One

told her then that she a - lone Would rule my life for - ev - er.
week and I'll be back a - gain, So do not be down - heart-ed."

told her then that she a - lone Would rule my life for - ev - er.
week and I'll be back a - gain, So do not be down - heart - ed."

Gypsy Violin

After the original by
LORRAINE N. FINLEY

1. What vi - o - lin has more ro-mance Than this one you are
2. Your vi - o - lin is ver - y old, Sur - viv - ing all dis-

1. What has more ro - mance, You are
2. Yours is ver - y old, All dis-

play - ing? O gyp - sy, can we guess per-chance The
as - ter; It once knew hands that now are cold And

play - ing? O gyp - sy, can we guess per - chance,
as - ter; It once knew hands that now are cold,

mes - sage you're con - vey - ing? O gyp - sy, though you
white as al - a - bas - ter. O gyp - sy, it was

You're con - vey - ing? Gyp - sy, though you
Al - a - bas - ter. Gyp - sy, it was

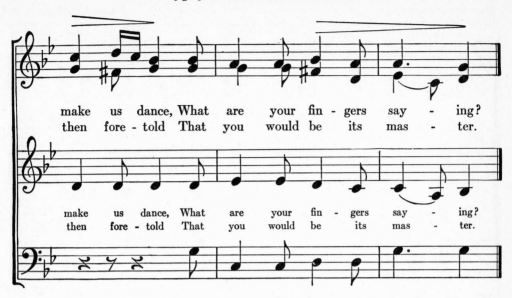

make us dance, What are your fin - gers say - ing?
then fore - told That you would be its mas - ter.

make us dance, What are your fin - gers say - ing?
then fore - told That you would be its mas - ter.

The Glorious Gift

Translated by
CHRISTINE TURNER CURTIS

GERMAN CAROL

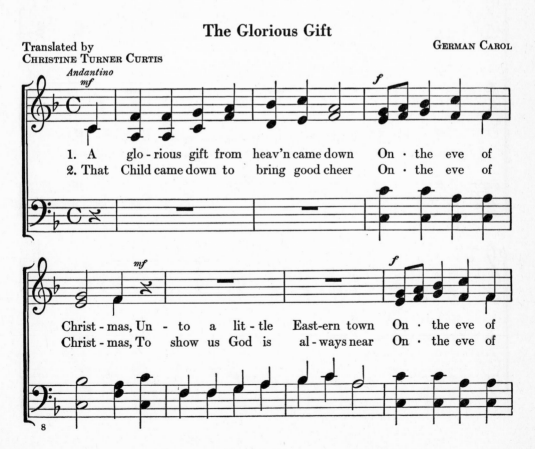

1. A glo - rious gift from heav'n came down On · the eve of
2. That Child came down to bring good cheer On · the eve of

Christ - mas, Un - to a lit - tle East - ern town On · the eve of
Christ - mas, To show us God is al - ways near On · the eve of

8

Christ - mas. This pre - cious gift God · free - ly sent
Christ - mas. While bright - ly shone the · skies a - bove

From the star - ry · fir - ma - ment For our hope and our con -
He de - scend - ed · like a dove, Lord of peace and Prince of

tent. An - gel hosts in spot - less white Sang · on high that
love. Now His ho - ly name we hail, Who · un - to that

ho - ly night Hymns of grave and pure de - light.
East - ern vale Came a ti - ny · In - fant frail.

KATHLEEN CARNES

FRENCH CAROL

1. While the wea - ry shep-herds sleep 'Mid si - lence low - ly,
2. Shep-herds, wake, the night is past! Sing forth the sto - ry.

An - gel guards their watch do keep O'er One so ho - ly.
Un - to us has come at last Light, hope, and glo - ry.

Then the Star a - bove the hills Earth with its glo - ry fills.
With the an - gels raise your voice, All men may now re - joice.

Joy and peace this bless - ed morn, (this morn) The Christ is born. ·
Joy and peace this bless - ed morn, (this morn) The Christ is born. ·

Break Forth, O Beauteous Heavenly Light

From the "Christmas Oratorio"   JOHANN SEBASTIAN BACH

Break forth, O beau - teous heav'n - ly light, And ush - er in the

morn - ing; Ye shep-herds, shrink not with af - fright, But

hear the an - gel's warn - ing. This Child, now weak in

in - fan - cy, Our con - fi - dence and joy shall be, The

pow'r of Sa - tan break - ing, Our peace e - ter - nal mak - ing.

Lo! Jesus Lies Cradled

PIERSON UNDERWOOD   RUSSIAN CAROL

Dolce espressivo

1. Lo! Je - sus lies cra - dled in an
2. Where wrap - pings warm gen - tly are en -

ox stall: Small new - born is heav - en's King! 'Neath
fold - ing, Low He lies in fra - grant hay While

win - try skies, shep-herds, though your flocks call Who will run sweet songs to
Ma - ry's arm safe the Child is hold - ing. Jo-seph sings : "By, by, lul-

sing? Hur - ry, hur - ry, shep - herds, run - ning to the Man - ger! For the
lay." By their gen - tle breath - ing sheep and kine shall warm Him, Where they

Lord of earth and sky, Play and sing soft lull - a - by!
share their hum - ble stall With the Lord Who made us all.

Sing, Ye Faithful, Sing

Translated from the French

FRENCH CAROL

1. Sing, ye faith - ful, sing No - ël, No - ël to - day. Christ is born a King, So lift your hearts and pray. Whit - er than curd There bloomed a flow'r-ing tree, On it sat a bird, And loud and clear sang he.

2. "Shep-herds, leave your sheep, To Beth - le - hem re - pair. Wrapped in ho - ly sleep An In - fant waits you there. Kings at His feet Lay frank - in - cense and spice, All the air is sweet With scents of Par - a - dise."

3. Sing, ye faith - ful, sing No - ël, No - ël to - day. Christ is born a King, So lift your hearts and pray. O - ver Him flew A gen - tle tur - tle - dove. Christ has brought to you The gifts of peace and love.

Oh Come, All Ye Faithful

ADESTE FIDELES

13th Century Latin
Translated by F. OAKELEY

Andante ben marcato

1. Oh come, all ye faith - ful, Joy-ful and tri -
2. Sing, choirs of An - gels, Sing in ex - ul -
A - des - te, fi - de - les, Lae - ti tri - um -

um - phant, Oh come ye, Oh come · ye to Beth - le - hem;
ta - tion, · Sing, all ye cit - i - zens of heav'n · a - bove:
phan - tes, Ve - ni - te, ve - ni - te in Beth - le - hem.

Come and be - hold Him Born the King of An - gels;
Glo - ry to God · In · the · high - est;
Na - tum vi - de - te, Re - gem an - ge - lo - rum.

O come, let us a - dore Him, O come, let us a -
Ve - ni - te, a - do - re - mus, Ve - ni - te, a - do -

dore Him, O come, let us a - dore Him, Christ, · the Lord.
re - mus, Ve - ni - te, a - do - re - mus Do - mi - num.

A Child Is Born

Translated from the original

Seth Calvisius (1556–1615)
Harmonized by Johann Sebastian Bach

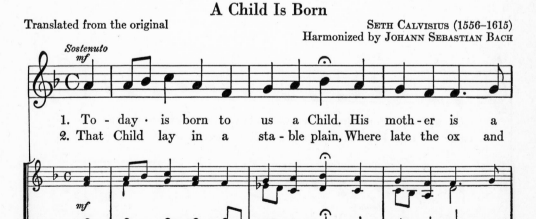

1. To - day · is born to us a Child. His moth - er is a
2. That Child lay in a sta - ble plain, Where late the ox and

O Little Town of Bethlehem[1]

PHILLIPS BROOKS

LEWIS REDNER

1. O lit - tle town of Beth - le-hem, How still we · see thee lie! A -
2. O ho - ly Child of Beth - le-hem, De-scend to · us, we pray; Cast

bove thy deep and dream - less sleep The si - lent stars go by; Yet
out our sin, and en - ter in; Be born in · us to - day. We

in thy dark street shin - eth The ev - er - last - ing Light; The
hear the Christ-mas an - gels The great glad tid - ings tell; Oh,

hopes and fears of all the years Are met in thee to - night.
come to us, a - bide with us, Our Lord Em-man - u - el!

[1] This song may be sung in unison if desired.

MARGUERITE DAVIS

The Jolly Beggar

ABBIE FARWELL BROWN

PHYLLIS BROWN FREEMAN

der - ry, Der - ry, der - ry, down, down, all the day.
der - ry, Der - ry, der - ry, down, down, all the day.

der - ry, der - ry, down, Der - ry, der - ry, der - ry, down, all the day.
der - ry, der - ry, down, Der - ry, der - ry, der - ry, down, all the day.

When Dreams Come True

Paraphrased by
CHRISTINE TURNER CURTIS

IRISH FOLK SONG

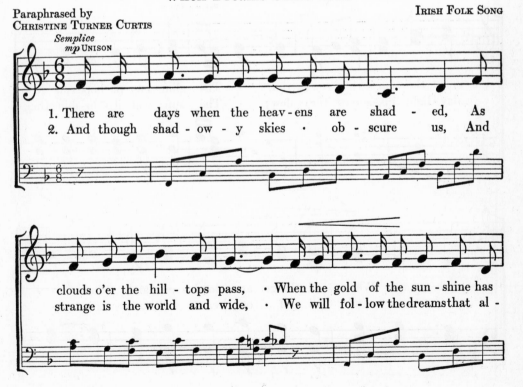

1. There are days when the heav - ens are shad - ed, As
2. And though shad - ow - y skies · ob - scure us, And

clouds o'er the hill - tops pass, · When the gold of the sun - shine has
strange is the world and wide, · We will fol - low the dreams that al -

fad - ed, And shad - ows de - scend on the grass.
lure us, With hope for our bea - con and guide.

Two part *cres*

Then hope sheds a lus - tre be - fore us A -
Then morn - ing will scat - ter the shad - ows As

dim.

Parts optional
mp

cross the ho - ri - zon's rim. · The glim - mer of hope can re -
day - light dis - solves the dew; · The sun will il - lu - mine the

store us When all things are cloud - ed and dim. ·
mead - ows, And all of our dreams will come true. ·

Pop! Goes the Weasel

RECREATION SONG

TRADITIONAL

TRADITIONAL
Arranged by PHYLLIS BROWN FREEMAN

Allegretto

1. All a-round the cob-bler's bench, The mon-key chased the wea-sel, The mon-key thought 'twas all · in fun, Pop! goes the wea-sel! I've no time to wait · or sigh, No pa-tience to wait till by and by; Kiss me quick, I'm off, good by! Pop! goes the wea-sel!

2. A pen-ny for a spool · of thread, A pen-ny for a nee-dle, That's the way the mon-ey goes; Pop! goes the wea-sel! John-ny's got the whoop-ing cough, And Jen - ny's got the mea - sles; That's the way the mon-ey goes, Pop! goes the wea-sel!

Song of the Plains

Translated by
HANNAH BAILEY

1. A - bove the wide and sol - emn plain, The sul - len clouds are brood - ing. Like flock - ing birds they gath - er fast, · The clouds that bring the snow. · Fill up your bins and your

2. The time has come to mend the fire, To tune the bal - a - lai - ka. The time has come, my broth - ers all, · To flee from out the cold, · To tell your tales and to

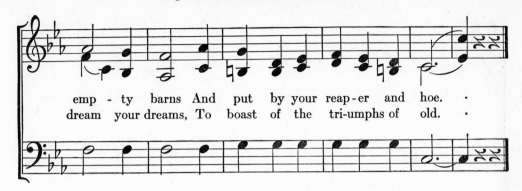

emp - ty barns And put by your reap-er and hoe.
dream your dreams, To boast of the tri-umphs of old.

Come, All You Worthy Christian Men

Adapted by
FRANCES FORD

ENGLISH FOLK SONG
Arranged by MARJORIE BROOKS

1. Come, all you wor-thy · Chris - tian men, That
2. Come, all you wor-thy · Chris - tian men, From

dwell up-on · this land, Don't spend your time in · care - less ways, But
doubt and fear re - frain, And bear your lot with cheer - ful hearts Nor

lend   a   help - ing   hand.   Be · watch - ful   of   your
grum - ble   nor · com - plain.   Some   men   are   rich   in

Second part optional

neigh - bor's good,   Be · mer - ci - ful   to ·   all.   There are
goods and lands,   And   oth - ers   beg   for ·   bread.   Yet we

man - y chang - es ·   in   this world,   Some   rise while oth - ers   fall.
all must give   a · strict ac - count,   The   Ho - ly Book has   said.

Blue Niemen

Translated

POLISH FOLK SONG

1. From blue Nie-men's marsh-y shores, Plain-tive riv-er
2. On blue Nie-men's fer-tile plains Wave the green and

Marsh-y shores,
Fer-tile plains,

mu-sic soars. Cry of the her-on in the reeds and
shin-ing grains. Snow of the buck-wheat, sil-ver of the

Mu-sic soars. Cry of the her-on in the reeds and
Shin-ing grains. Snow of the buck-wheat, sil-ver of the

rush-es, Through the north-ern twi-light pours.
rye-fields, Nour-ished by the north-ern rains.

rush-es, Through the north-ern twi-light pours.
rye-fields, Nour-ished by the north-ern rains.

Hail, Glorious Mountain Land

M. Bühler
Translated

Otto Barblan

1. Hail, glo-rious moun-tain land, Where peaks at morn-ing stand
2. Cloud-shad-owed moun-tain land, Strong hearts thy skies de-mand,

1. Hail, glo-rious moun-tain land, Where peaks at morn-ing stand
2. Cloud-shad-owed moun-tain land, Strong hearts thy skies de-mand,

Crowned with rain - bow haze. Out of the ice and night,
Loft - y lives and pure. Peace like a gen - tle dove

Crowned with rain - bow haze. Out of the ice and night,
Loft - y lives - and pure. Peace like a gen - tle dove

Shin - ing with dawn - a - light, Rise thy sum - mits
Looks from thy stars - a - bove. Of - fer - ings of

Shin - ing with dawn - a - light, Rise thy sum - mits
Looks from thy stars - a - bove. Of - fer - ings of

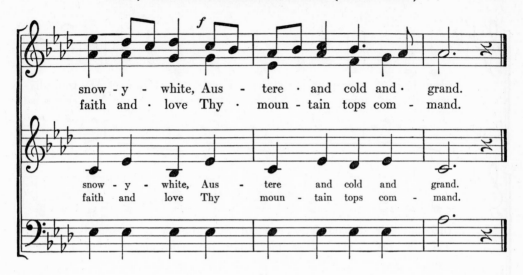

snow - y - white, Aus - tere · and cold and · grand.
faith and · love Thy · moun - tain tops com - mand.

snow - y - white, Aus - tere and cold and grand.
faith and love Thy moun - tain tops com - mand.

Flow Gently, Sweet Afton[1]

RECREATION SONG

ROBERT BURNS

JAMES E. SPILMAN

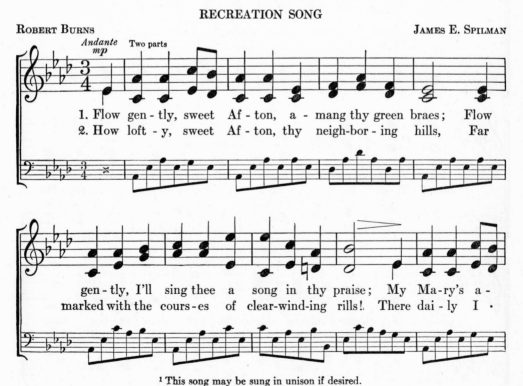

1. Flow gen - tly, sweet Af - ton, a - mang thy green braes; Flow
2. How loft - y, sweet Af - ton, thy neigh-bor - ing hills, Far

gen - tly, I'll sing thee a song in thy praise; My Ma-ry's a -
marked with the cours - es of clear-wind-ing rills! There dai - ly I ·

[1] This song may be sung in unison if desired.

Pirate Song

CHRISTINE TURNER CURTIS

LILY STRICKLAND

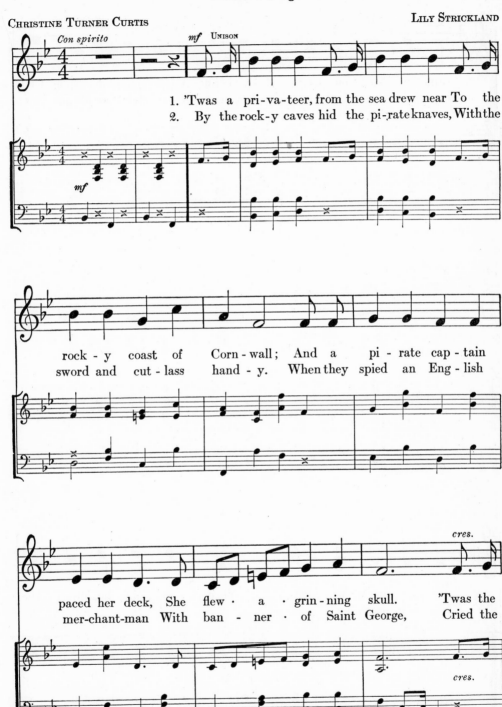

1. 'Twas a pri-va-teer, from the sea drew near To the
2. By the rock-y caves hid the pi-rate knaves, With the

rock - y coast of Corn - wall; And a pi - rate cap - tain
sword and cut - lass hand - y. When they spied an Eng - lish

paced her deck, She flew a grin - ning skull. 'Twas the
mer-chant-man With ban - ner of Saint George, Cried the

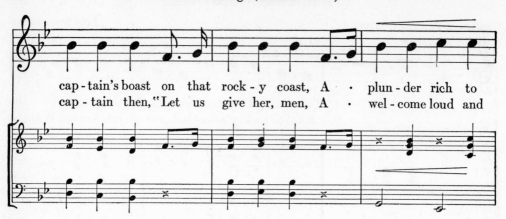

cap - tain's boast on that rock - y coast, A · plun - der rich to
cap - tain then, "Let us give her, men, A · wel - come loud and

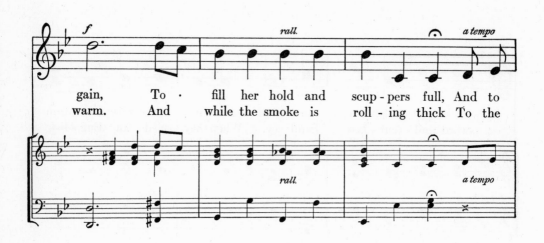

gain,   To · fill her hold and scup - pers full, And to
warm.   And while the smoke is roll - ing thick To the

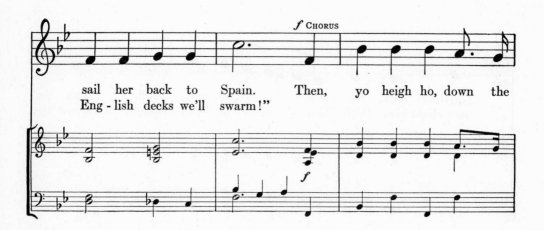

sail her back to Spain.   Then, yo heigh ho, down the
Eng - lish decks we'll swarm!"

seas we'll go, With the boo - ty · in our hold. Through the

rac - ing foam we will head her home, With a

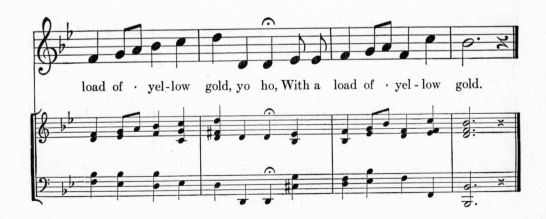

load of · yel-low gold, yo ho, With a load of · yel-low gold.

The Wedding[1]

Translated by
PIERSON UNDERWOOD

POLISH FOLK SONG
Arranged by LAWRENCE PERRY

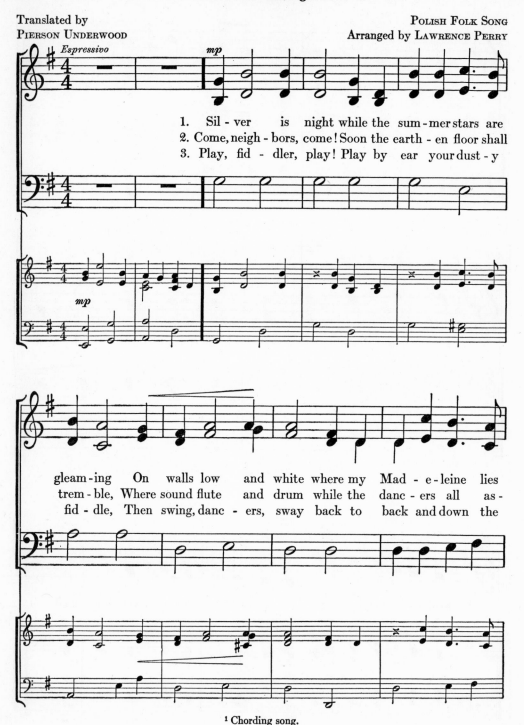

1. Sil - ver is night while the sum - mer stars are
2. Come, neigh - bors, come! Soon the earth - en floor shall
3. Play, fid - dler, play! Play by ear your dust - y

gleam - ing On walls low and white where my Mad - e - leine lies
trem - ble, Where sound flute and drum while the danc - ers all as -
fid - dle, Then swing, danc - ers, sway back to back and down the

[1] Chording song.

dream-ing! Her eyes, dark yet bright, no light of star need bor-row. Come
sem - ble! Let boots stamp the floor while wide, bright skirts are whirl-ing, Till
mid - dle! Till morn - ing dawns gold while still the dance we're tread-ing, My

soon, morn - ing light, for the dawn-ing · brings a joy - ful mor-row.
day-light shall pour and the dawn shall · hush the mu - sic skirl - ing.
Mag - da I'll hold to my heart! Sing hey! the mer - ry wed-ding.

Alouette

RECREATION SONG

FRENCH-CANADIAN FOLK SONG

A - lou-et - te, gen-tille a - lou-et - te, A - lou-et - te,

je te plu - me-rai. A - lou-et - te, gen - tille a - lou-et - te,

A - lou-et - te, je te plu-me-rai.   1. Je te plu - me-rai la tête,
2. Je te plu - me-rai le bec,

Je te plu - me-rai la tête!   Et la tête, et la tête!
Je te plu - me-rai le bec!   Et le bec, et le bec!

3. Je te plumerai le cou!
Je te plumerai le cou!
Et le cou, et le cou!
Et le bec, et le bec!
Et la tête, et la tête!
Alouette, alouette! Oh,

4. Je te plumerai le dos!
Je te plumerai le dos!
Et le dos, et le dos!
Et le cou, et le cou!
Et le bec, et le bec!
Et la tête, et la tête!
Alouette, alouette! Oh,

5. Et les pattes! (bis) Et le dos! (bis) Et le cou! (bis) Et le bec! (bis) Et la tête! (bis)
Alouette! (bis) Oh,

6. Et la queue! (bis) Et les pattes! (bis) Et le dos! (bis) Et le cou! (bis) Et le bec! (bis)
Et la tête! (bis) Alouette! (bis) Oh,

TRANSLATIONS: *Alouette:* lark — *gentille:* nice — *Je te plumerai la tête:*
I'll pluck the feathers from your head — *bec:* beak — *cou:* neck —
dos: back — *pattes:* feet — *queue:* tail.

Say Good-by

GOTTFRIED AUGUST BÜRGER
Translated

LUDWIG VAN BEETHOVEN

1. Say good - by, and let no grief dis - tress you,
2. Say good - by, no tear of mine shall bind you.

Take nei - ther gold nor jew - els to op - press you.
Speak no re - grets, but leave the past be - hind you.

When your lone - ly way you take by moun - tain pass, by
Though you wan - der far and free, a - cross the land, a -

wood and lake, Then let thoughts of me a-wake, to cheer and bless you.
cross the sea, Where-so - ev - er you may be, my thoughts will find you.

Steal Away[1]

NEGRO SPIRITUAL

Steal a - way, steal a - way, steal a - way to Je - sus!

Steal a - way, steal a - way home, I have not long to stay here.

1. My Lord . . calls me, He calls me by the thun - der; The
2. My Lord . . calls me, He calls me by the light - ning; The

trum-pet sounds with - in a my soul: I have not long to stay here.

8

[1] This song may be sung in unison if desired.

Roadwells

JOHN MASEFIELD

KEITH CROSBY BROWN

One road leads to Lon - don,

One road leads to Wales, · My road leads me sea - ward To the

white drip - ping sails. · One road leads to the riv - er, As it

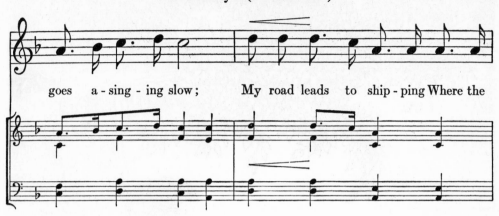

goes a - sing - ing slow; My road leads to ship - ping Where the

bronzed sail - ors go. It leads me, lures me, calls me To the

salt green toss-ing sea; A road with-out earth's road-dust Is the

MARGUERITE DAVIS

right road for me. A wet road, heav-ing, shin - ing, And

wild with sea - gulls' cries. A mad salt sea - wind blow - ing The

salt spray in my eyes. My road calls me, lures me,

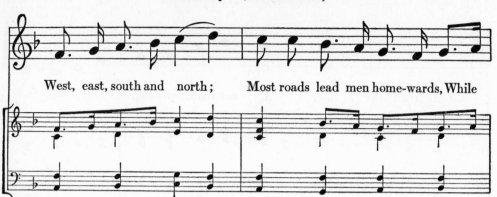

West, east, south and north;   Most roads lead men home-wards, While

my road leads me forth To add more miles to the tal-ly Of gray

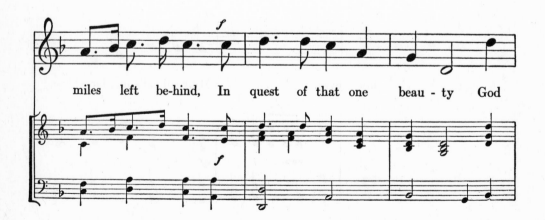

miles left be-hind, In quest of that one beau - ty God

put me here to find.

The Old Crusaders

Translated and adapted by
LORRAINE N. FINLEY

FRENCH-CANADIAN FOLK SONG
Arranged by MARION BAUER

Andante
mf

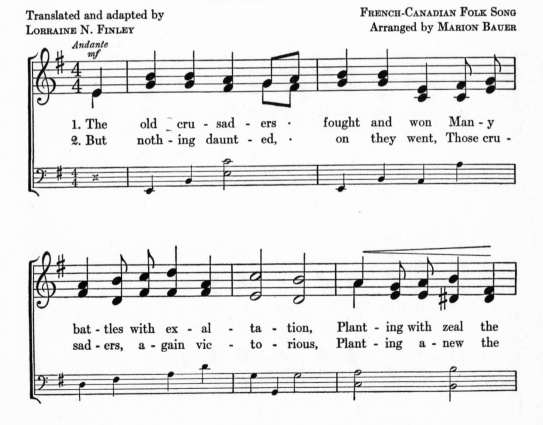

1. The old cru - sad - ers · fought and won Man - y
2. But noth - ing daunt - ed, · on they went, Those cru -

bat - tles with ex - al - ta - tion, Plant - ing with zeal the
sad - ers, a - gain vic - to - rious, Plant - ing a - new the

love of faith In the heart of our moth-er na - tion. But
love of faith With a sac - ri - fice that was glo - rious. With

e - vil came with a sear - ing flame When the
hearts a - flame, it shall be our aim To pro -

Parts optional
molto cres.

en - e - my, danc-ing and sing - ing Their war - like songs, o - ver -
tect what our fore - fa - thers left us. We brought from far, what their

f

threw the faith That had come to the heart of France.
hearts had won, To the home of our new - born France.

Translated from the original

ITALIAN FOLK SONG

1. Noon and
3. Ev - 'ry

morn - ing, day and night You are al - ways my de -
morn - ing we would sing Like the larks up - on the

light. Oh, how hap - py I would be If you'd
wing. I would work like an - y bee, If you'd

If (Continued)

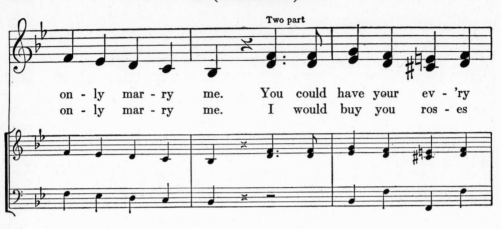

on - ly mar - ry me. You could have your ev - 'ry
on - ly mar - ry me. I would buy you ros - es

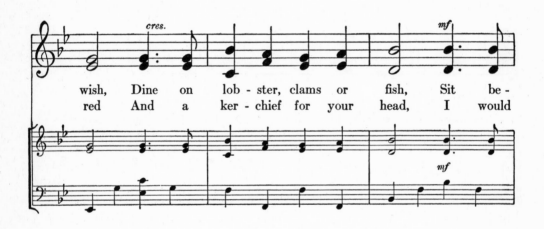

wish, Dine on lob - ster, clams or fish, Sit be -
red And a ker - chief for your head, I would

neath a shad - y tree, If you'd on - ly mar - ry me.
heed your ev - 'ry plea, If you'd on - ly mar - ry me.

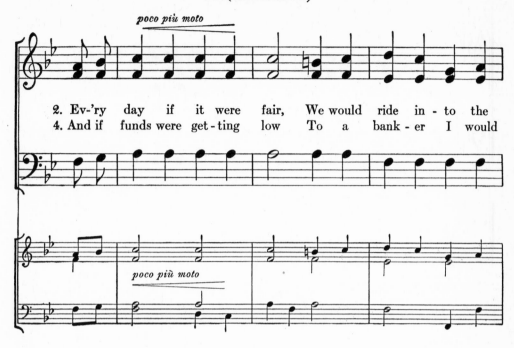

2. Ev-'ry day if it were fair, We would ride in - to the
4. And if funds were get-ting low To a bank - er I would

air By the edg - es of the sea If you'd on - ly mar - ry
go, To a loan he would a - gree If you'd on - ly mar - ry

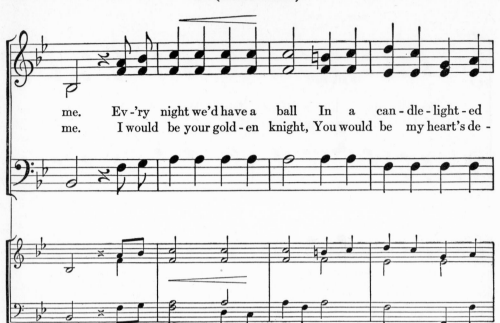

me.   Ev-'ry night we'd have a   ball   In a   can-dle-light-ed

me.   I would be your gold-en knight, You would be   my heart's de-

hall.   We'd have hon-ey with our   tea,   If   you'd on-ly mar-ry   me.

light.   Oh, how hap-py we could be,   If   you'd on-ly mar-ry   me.

ANONYMOUS

Arranged from ROSSINI

1. To · Him from Whom our bless - ings flow, Who all our wants sup - plies, ·
2. 'Twas He who led the pil - grim band A - cross the storm - y sea; ·
3. Be · Thou our na - tion's strength and shield In · man-hood and in youth; ·

This day the cho - ral song and vow · From grate-ful hearts shall rise. ·
'Twas He who stayed the ty - rant's hand And set our coun - try free. ·
Thine arm for our pro - tec - tion wield, And guide us by Thy truth. ·

On the Hoogli River

Translated and adapted by
LILY STRICKLAND

BENGALI INDIAN FOLK SONG

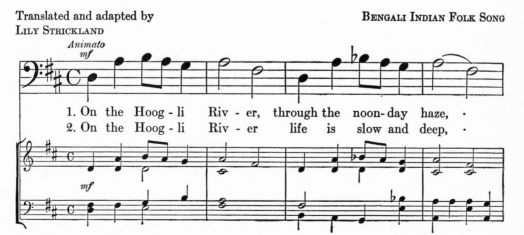

1. On the Hoog - li Riv - er, through the noon-day haze, ·
2. On the Hoog - li Riv - er life is slow and deep, ·

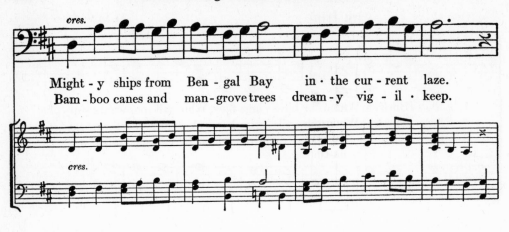

Might - y ships from   Ben - gal Bay   in · the cur - rent   laze.
Bam - boo canes and   man - grove trees   dream - y vig - il · keep.

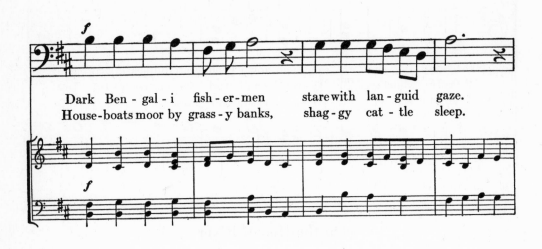

Dark Ben - gal - i   fish - er - men   stare with lan - guid   gaze.
House - boats moor by grass - y banks,   shag - gy cat - tle   sleep.

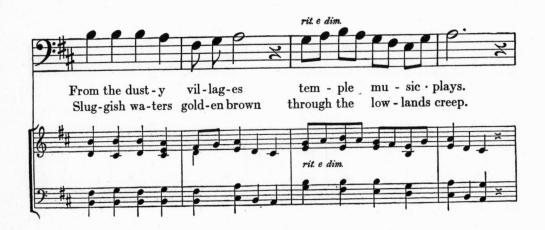

From the dust - y   vil - lag - es   tem - ple _ mu - sic · plays.
Slug - gish wa - ters gold - en brown   through the   low - lands creep.

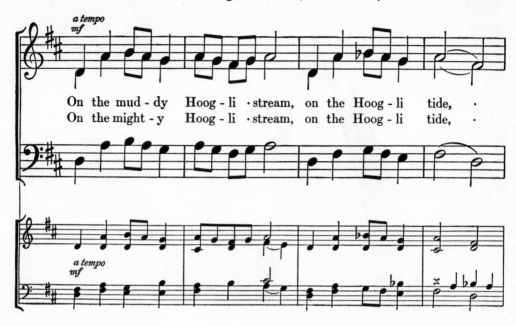

On the mud - dy Hoog - li ·stream, on the Hoog - li tide, ·
On the might - y Hoog - li ·stream, on the Hoog - li tide, ·

Through the rice fields green and wide; Rice fields ver - y · green and wide. ·
Man - y ships at · an-chor ride; Man- y ships at · an - chor ride. ·

The Fishing Fleet

Pierson Underwood

French Folk Tune
Arranged by Lawrence Perry

1. The fish-ing fleet goes out with the dawn, (Heave the an - chor
2. Now sweet-hearts all must wait on the shore, (Caps gleam white as

in!) While sleep - y towns-folk stum-ble and yawn, We our day - be -
snow!) Till twi - light brings the ships · once more Through the af - ter -

gin. Our col - ored sails of red and blue Shall tint the morn-ing
glow! Each sail and rope and mast and spar In sun glows ros - y -

mist, Till far · at sea they melt from view In haze of am - e - thyst!
red, Till mast - lights pass the har - bor bar, And an - chors drop to bed.

8

Then o-ver the wa-ter our boats shall sail What-ev-er the wind or the
Then o-ver the rip-ple the boats row in, All gleam-ing with fish in the

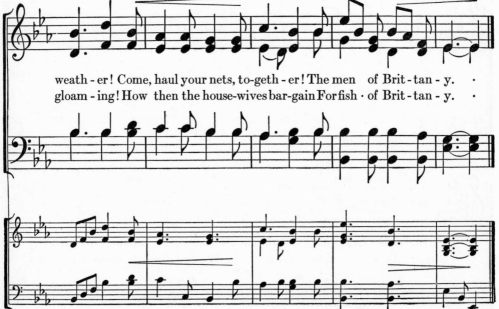

weath-er! Come, haul your nets, to-geth-er! The men of Brit-tan-y.
gloam-ing! How then the house-wives bar-gain For fish of Brit-tan-y.

The Lone Fish-ball

STUDENT COLLECTION

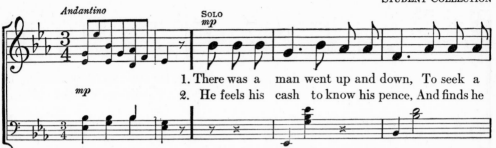

1. There was a man went up and down, To seek a
2. He feels his cash to know his pence, And finds he

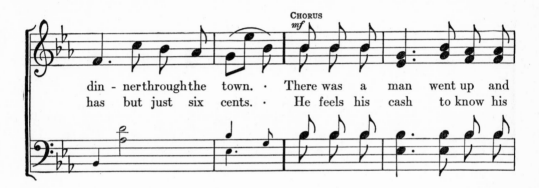

din - ner through the town. · There was a man went up and
has but just six cents. · He feels his cash to know his

down, To seek a din - ner through the town.
pence, And finds he has but just six cents.

3. He finds at last a right cheap place,
   And enters in with modest face.

4. The bill of fare he searches through,
   To see what his six cents will do.

5. The cheapest viand of them all
   Is "Twelve and a half cents for *two* Fish-ball."

6. The waiter he to him doth call,
   And gently whispers — "*one* Fish-ball."

7. The waiter roars it through the hall,
   The guests they start at "*one* Fish-ball!"

8. The man then says, quite ill at ease,
   "A piece of bread, sir, if you please."

9. The waiter roars it through the hall,
   "We don't give bread with *one* Fish-ball!"

MORAL

10. Who would have bread with his Fish-ball,
    Must get it first, or not at all.

11. Who would Fish-ball with *fixings* eat,
    Must get some friend to stand a treat.

Quiet Hearts[1]

CHRISTINE TURNER CURTIS

FRANZ JOSEPH HAYDN

1. Qui - et hearts are like the pools Where the sun de - scend - ing
2. Qui - et hearts are like the lanes Full of li - lac shad - ows,

Min - gles gold and pearl - y green In a liq - uid blend - ing.
Where the shep-herds lead their flocks Home from sun - lit mead-ows.

Mir-rored on their sur - face cool Snow - y clouds are glid - ing,
All is tran-quil there and still, All is dim and dream-ing;

And their crys - tal deeps re - veal Ten - der thoughts con - fid - ing.
From the clam-ors of the world Trou-bled lives re - deem - ing.

[1] This song may be sung in unison if desired.

BEN JONSON   RECREATION SONG   OLD ENGLISH AIR

[1] This song may be sung in unison if desired.

March of the Fife and Drum Corps

John Sumner

Polish Folk Tune

Gypsy Weather

PIERSON UNDERWOOD

HUNGARIAN FOLK TUNE
Arranged by LAWRENCE PERRY

1. Come with me!'Tis gyp - sy weath - er!
2. Come with me! The dance is whirl - ing,

Come, come, lad and lass! Wind and wood-smoke drift to-geth-er,
Wild, wild whirls the throng. Where the camp-fire smoke is curl-ing,

Low, low bends the grass. Fol-low dusk, dream-ing, Where star-light is
High, high rings the song. Wild the notes ring - ing, Where danc-ers are

gleam-ing. O gyp-sy fire, kin-dling Where twi-light is dwin-dling, Oh!
swing-ing, All rest and sleep scorn-ing Till frost - y comes morn-ing, Oh!

Deep River

NEGRO SPIRITUAL

UNISON or SOLO

Deep · · · riv - er, my home is o - ver Jor-dan, ·

Deep · · · riv - er, Lord, I want to cross o - ver in - to camp-ground.

Deep ... riv-er, my home is o-ver Jor-dan, ...

Deep ... riv-er, Lord, I want to cross o-ver in-to camp-ground.

Oh, don't you want to go · to the gos-pel ...

feast, · That prom - ised land · where all · is

Deep River (Continued)

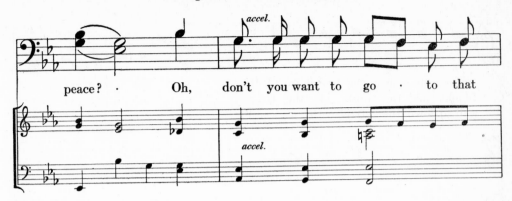

peace? Oh, don't you want to go to that

prom - ised land, that land where all is peace?

Abdullah Bulbul Amir

STUDENT COLLECTION

UNKNOWN

Allegro

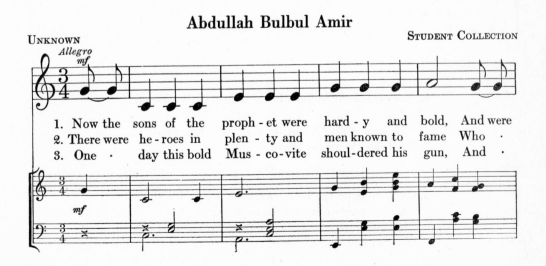

1. Now the sons of the proph - et were hard - y and bold, And were
2. There were he - roes in plen - ty and men known to fame Who
3. One day this bold Mus - co - vite shoul - dered his gun, And

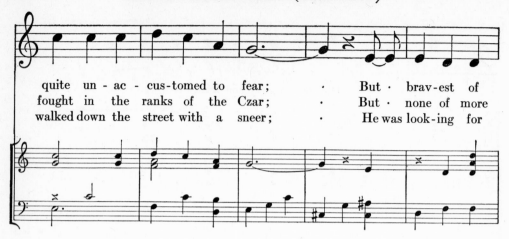

quite un-ac-cus-tomed to fear; . But · brav-est of
fought in the ranks of the Czar; . But · none of more
walked down the street with a sneer; . He was look-ing for

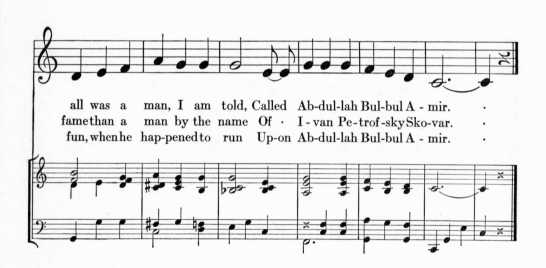

all was a man, I am told, Called Ab-dul-lah Bul-bul A - mir. .
fame than a man by the name Of · I-van Pe-trof-sky Sko-var. .
fun, when he hap-pened to run Up-on Ab-dul-lah Bul-bul A - mir. .

4. Then this bold Mameluke drew his trusty chibouk,
   Saying, "Send your regards to the Czar!"
   And with willful intent he most suddenly went
   For Ivan Petrofsky Skovar.

5. On a stone by the banks where Neva doth roll,
   There is written in characters clear:
   "Oh, Stranger, remember to pray for the soul
   Of Abdullah Bulbul Amir."

Prayer at Morning

FRANCES FORD

GEORGE FREDERIC HANDEL

Bless us and keep us, Through dawn and day-light,
Bless us, and guide us In - to Thy ha - ven.

Be Thou our · bea-con To set · our steps a - right. Shine on our
Lead us, O · · Fa-ther, To Thy · heav-en-ly light.

path-way, Bring ra - diant noon-day To blaze on our · sight.

The Traveler

After the original by
CHRISTINE TURNER CURTIS

POLISH FOLK SONG
Arranged by LAWRENCE PERRY

1. Jo - sef, when first you sal - ly forth, Wheth - er to west or
2. Climb not the loft - y moun - tain wall Lest you should lose your

east or north, Take not the white · and broad high - way,
head and fall. Sail not where sap - phire wa - ters leap,

Lest thieves and rob - bers you be - tray. Tread not at night the
Lest waves should drown you in the deep. Jo - sef, 'tis bet - ter

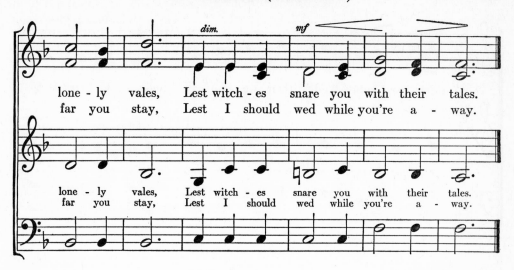

lone - ly vales, Lest witch - es snare you with their tales.
far you stay, Lest I should wed while you're a - way.

lone - ly vales, Lest witch - es snare you with their tales.
far you stay, Lest I should wed while you're a - way.

A Catch

ANONYMOUS

PHYLLIS BROWN FREEMAN

When V and · I to - geth - er meet We ·

make up · six in house or street: Yet I and V may

Yet I and V may

W. S. GILBERT

ARTHUR S. SULLIVAN
From "Patience"

1. A mag-net hung in a hard-ware shop, And all a-round was a lov-ing crop Of scis-sors and nee-dles, nails and knives, Of-fer-ing love for all · their lives; But for i-ron the mag-net

2. And iron and steel ex-pressed sur-prise, The nee-dles o-pened their well-drilled eyes, The pen-knives · felt "shut up," no doubt, The scis-sors de-clared them-selves "cut out," The · ket-tles they boiled with

[1] The accompaniment has been simplified from the original version.

felt no whim,   Though he charm - ed i-ron, it
rage, 'tis said,   While · ev - 'ry nail · went

charmed not him, From nee - dles and nails · and knives he'd turn, For he'd
off its head, And hith-er and · thith-er be - gan to roam Till a

set · his love · on a sil - ver churn!   A sil - ver churn!
ham-mer came up · and · drove them home.   It drove them home?

A sil - ver churn!   His most aes - thet - ic, ver-y mag-net-ic ·
It drove them home;   While this mag - net - ic, per-i-pa - tet - ic ·

The Coachman

English version by
PIERSON UNDERWOOD

RUSSIAN FOLK SONG

Jog on in the mist and fad-ing light! · Jog on, tired

Wea-

horse, wea-ry man! · Past days like a dream of the night · Go

ry man! · Days like a dream of the night · Go

by with our trun-dling car-a - van! · The friends of my youth, they are

gone! · Good coach-man, drive slow - ly, I pray. · None waits while your

Slow I pray ·

hors - es jog on, · Jog on in the dusk of the day. ·

The Faithful Lass

Adapted from the original

SCOTCH FOLK SONG

1. There is mu - sic and mirth on the green by the
2. Though an earl or a duke they could find me to

wil - lows, Yet here I sit lone - ly be - side my cot - tage
mar - ry, Though pearls I could wear that were fit for an - y

door. I think of my Don-al a-way on the bil-lows, I
queen, I'll bide me at home and for Don-al I'll tar-ry, His

pic-ture him sail-ing a-long a for-eign shore.
laugh-ter so bon-ny, his eyes so blue and keen.

America the Beautiful[1]

KATHARINE LEE BATES   SAMUEL A. WARD

Maestoso
f

1. O beau - ti - ful for spa - cious skies, For am - ber waves of grain, · For
2. O beau - ti - ful for pil - grim feet whose stern im - pas - sioned stress · A
3. O beau - ti - ful for he - roes proved In lib - er - at - ing strife, · Who
4. O beau - ti - ful for pa - triot dream That sees be - yond the years · Thine

pur - ple moun - tain maj - es - ties A - bove the fruit - ed plain! · A -
thor - ough-fare for free - dom beat A - cross the wil - der - ness! · A -
more than self their coun - try loved, And mer - cy more than life! · A -
al - a - bas - ter cit - ies gleam Un - dimmed by hu - man tears! · A -

mer - i - ca! A - mer - i - ca! God shed His grace on thee, · And
mer - i - ca! A - mer - i - ca! God mend thine ev - 'ry flaw, · Con -
mer - i - ca! A - mer - i - ca! May God thy gold re - fine · Till
mer - i - ca! A - mer - i - ca! God shed His grace on thee · And

crown thy good with broth - er - hood, From sea to shin - ing sea!
firm thy soul in self - con-trol, Thy lib - er - ty in law!
all suc - cess be no - ble - ness, And ev - 'ry gain di - vine!
crown thy good with broth - er - hood From sea to shin - ing sea!

[1] This may be sung in unison if desired.

The Hurdy-Gurdy

English version by
HANNAH BAILEY

ITALIAN FOLK SONG
Arranged by LAWRENCE PERRY

1. A maid-en, plump and stur-dy, Turned an
2. So then I grew more word-y. "Let me

an-cient hur-dy-gur-dy. I said, in ac-cents breez-y, "Why that
try your hur-dy-gur-dy. The wheez-ing we can mas-ter If we

in-stru-ment is wheez-y!" Tra la lu-ra! Oh, noth-ing could be
on-ly turn it fast-er." Tra la lu-ra! Her glance was e-ven

¹ This may be sung in unison. In that case unchanged voices will sing an octave higher.

cool - er, Tra la lu - ra! Than the way she looked at me.
cool - er, Tra la lu - ra! Than the i - cy Po - lar sea.

Hayfoot, Strawfoot

John Sumner

Anna von W. Grille

Con anima
mf

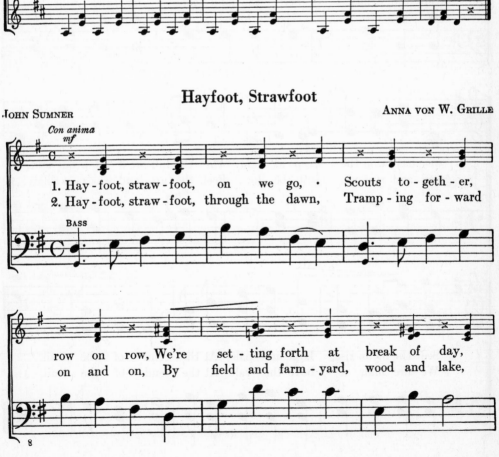

1. Hay - foot, straw - foot, on we go, · Scouts to - geth - er,
2. Hay - foot, straw - foot, through the dawn, Tramp - ing for - ward

Bass

row on row, We're set - ting forth at break of day,
on and on, By field and farm - yard, wood and lake,

8

Parts optional

Night will · find us far a - way. Hay - foot, straw - foot,
Sing - ing · till the ech - oes wake! Hay - foot, straw - foot,

cres.

up we climb, · Keep the rhyth - m all the time, When
keep the stride, · See the land-scape far and wide Lie

f

we have won the steep as - cent. On the hill we'll pitch our tent,
green and sun-ny just be - low. Feel the up - land breez - es blow!

See the moon rise, large and pale, At the end of the trail.
We are high a - bove the vale At the end of the trail.

RECREATION SONG

William S. Pitts

William S. Pitts

1. There's a church in the val - ley by the wild - wood, No
2. How sweet on a bright · Sab - bath morn - ing To

love - li - er place in the dale; No · spot is so dear to my
list to the clear ring-ing bell; Its · tones so · sweet - ly are

child - hood As the lit - tle brown · church in the vale. ·
call - ing, O · come · to the church in the vale.

vale ; No spot is so dear to my

come, come, come, No · spot is so dear to my

After second verse, repeat Chorus *pp*

child - hood As the lit - tle brown church in the vale.

After the original by
CHRISTINE TURNER CURTIS

DANISH FOLK SONG

1. From door to door and from town to town Goes the
2. By farm and mill, at the ear-ly dawn Goes the

scis-sor-grind-er, · up and down, And · with-out end his ·
scis-sor-grind-er · push-ing on. · When chil-dren stare and ·

cries as-cend, "Bring your knives and scis-sors, I im-plore you!"
house-wives glare, In the o-pen air he finds his free-dom.

When good for-tune is smil-ing He de-clares his work is be-
All the world is his rich-es, Though he sleeps in fields or in

cres.

guil - ing   And he   takes his · meals like   birds   on the wing, While
ditch - es,   And he   has   re - ward for   long wea-ry miles When

f   Parts optional

clangs the bell   a-din-gle,   din - gle, ding.1, 2. Some days are good, oth-er
pret - ty maids are gra-cious with their smiles.

days are poor, But the   life   of   a scis - sor-grind-er   has its lure.

A Norwegian Legend

KATHLEEN CARNES

NORWEGIAN MELODY

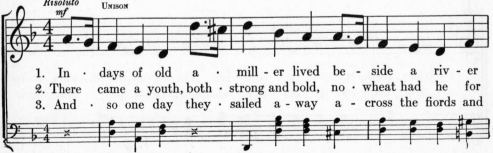

Risoluto
mf   UNISON

1. In · days of old   a · mill - er lived be - side a   riv - er
2. There   came a youth, both · strong and bold, no · wheat had he for
3. And · so one day they · sailed a - way   a - cross the fiords and

wind - ing, And · all the farm - ers from a - round brought
grind - ing. But, · "Sir," he said, "I think I can re -
moun - tain, And · when they reached the Mid-night Sun drank

him their wheat for grind - ing. He · had a daugh - ter ·
move this si - lence bind - ing. We'll · trav - el to the ·
deep - ly from the foun - tain. The · maid knelt there and ·

sweet and fair, no love - lier maid dwelt an - y - where, Yet
Mid-night Sun where love - ly crys - tal wa - ters run With
drank un - til some words at last she'd spok - en, And

not one word had she spok - en, her · fa - ther's heart was brok - en.
mag - ic pow'r for · heal - ing if · one will drink there kneel - ing."
now her voice, it is nev - er still: her · fa - ther's heart is brok - en.

Here's to the Maiden

Adapted from the original

ENGLISH FOLK SONG

Allegretto moderato
mp

1. Here's to the maid - en of bash - ful fif - teen,
2. Here's to the maid - en whose dim - ples we prize!

1. Maid of shy fif - teen,
2. Dim - ples that we prize,

Here's to her laugh - ter be - guil - ing! Here's to her curls like the
Here's to the maid - en with none, sir! Here's to a girl with a

Charm be - guil - ing! Curls like
Some have none, sir! Pair of

crown of a queen, And here's to her chat - ter and smil - ing.
pair of blue eyes, And here's to the girl with but one, sir!

crown of queen; Here's to her mirth and smil - ing.
deep blue eyes, Or e - ven on - ly one, sir!

Hail to the maid, mer - ry or staid, Who's live - ly and sun - ny and

Hail · the maid, gay · or staid, Who's live - ly, sun - ny,

nev - er a - fraid. Here's to the maid, mer - ry or staid, Who's

un - a - fraid. Here's to the maid, mer - ry or staid, Who's

live - ly and sun - ny and nev - er a - fraid.

live - ly and sun - ny and nev - er a - fraid.

The Old House [1]

Adapted from the original

Scotch Folk Song

Dolce cantabile

1. The old house, the old house is emp-ty now and still, But
2. The mas-ter was live-ly, the la-dy she was fair, And

1. H'n
2. H'n

H'n kind hearts once beat there-in, and chil-dren played at will, The
H'n care-free the mer-ry days we passed in child-hood there, But

The But

cres.

wild rose and the jes-sa-mine grew thick up-on the wall, And
all of us are scat-tered now to oth-er lands and leas, And

rose and jes-sa-mine grew thick up-on the wall, And
we are scat-tered now to oth-er lands and leas, And

[1] Humming parts are optional.

man - y   are   the   mem - 'ries their   per - fume can   re - call.
some lie   in   the   kirk - yard, and   some have crossed the seas.

Thou Art Near Me, Margarita

ERIK MEYER-HELMUND

1. When the waves are   gen - tly flow - ing,
2. When the   rug - ged   cliff · de - scend - ing,

In   the   eve - ning   red · all glow - ing,   When the day   is
To strange lands my   way · I'm bend - ing,   White the sea - foam

slow - ly · dy - ing, When a - far sweet bells are sigh - ing;
plays be - fore me, Through my · soul a dream comes o'er me;

1, 2. Thou · art near · me, Mar - ga - ri - ta!

Thou · · art near me, Mar - ga - ri - ta!

Thou · art near · me, Mar — ga - ri - ta! ·

Thou · art near me, Mar-ga - ri - ta!

North by West

Pierson Underwood

A SONG OF ALASKA

Lawrence Perry

1. Boats in the north! Lone - ly your fish - ing Where wa - ters
2. Stars of the north! Bright on the ice-fields, Or gray-green
3. North and by west! Jour - ney-ing lone - ly, By dog - sled

roll to the Po - lar Star! What are your fish - er - men
tun - dra,[1] where rein - deer roam, Clear - er you shine than the
trek - king, or sail - ing free. Seal - hunt - er, min - er, or

dream - ing, wish-ing? Where do their thoughts go, sail - ing far?
moon on rice-fields, Where yel - low riv - ers curl with foam!
rov - er on - ly. What is it calls, by land or sea?

Fish - ers of A - sia, from dis - tant is - lands, Tall men,
South-ward in A - sia the O - rient slum - bers, Short leagues
Trap - per or fish - er or west - ern rang - er, Tall trees

[1] A treeless plain in the Arctic regions.

out of the Land of the Bear, When home you trav-el, your
dis-tant, yet strange and a - far; In north-ern wa-ters we
lure us, and streams run-ning clear. North-ward we fol-low where

boats go west-ward: We · sail east to a land ·more fair!
hear new voic-es, Clear · as winds 'neath the Po - lar Star.
calls A - las - ka, North by west, to the Last Fron - tier!

The Question

After the original by
JOHN SUMNER

ITALIAN FOLK SONG

Con anima

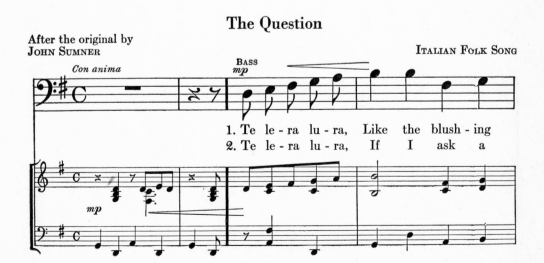

1. Te le - ra lu - ra, Like the blush - ing
2. Te le - ra lu - ra, If I ask a

ros - es, Sweet-er than the yel - low jas - mine flow - er, Te le - ra lu - ra,
ques-tion While her star-ry eyes are veiled and shy, · Te le - ra lu - ra,

Smiles my dam - i - gèl - la Look-ing from her green and leaf - y
Will she deign to lis - ten? Will she ev - er give me her re -

bow - er. Te le - ra lu - ra, If by an - y
ply? · Te le - ra lu - ra, If by an - y

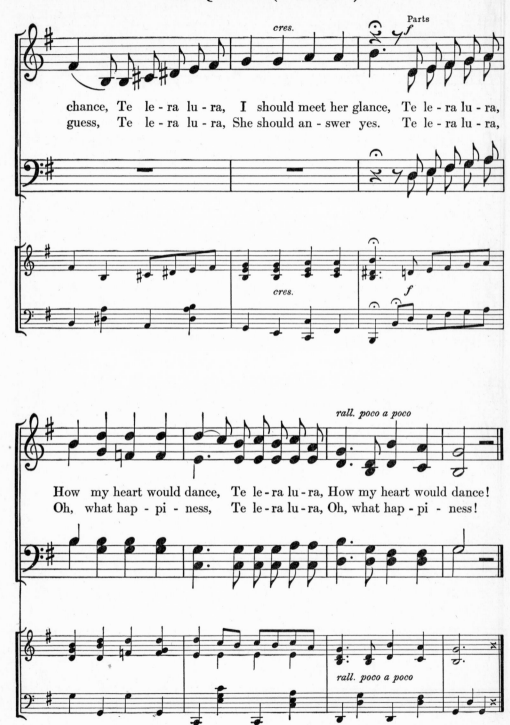

chance, Te le - ra lu - ra, I should meet her glance, Te le - ra lu - ra,
guess, Te le - ra lu - ra, She should an - swer yes. Te le - ra lu - ra,

How my heart would dance, Te le - ra lu - ra, How my heart would dance!
Oh, what hap - pi - ness, Te le - ra lu - ra, Oh, what hap - pi - ness!

Oh, Dem Golden Slippers

JAMES A. BLAND

JAMES A. BLAND

Bingo, the Dingo, and the Fatal Flamingo

LAURA E. RICHARDS

ROY NEWMAN

1. The Din-go, the Din-go, He went by the name · of
2. "Fla - min-go, Fla-min-go, Oh, say, will you wed · with
3. Fla - min-go, Fla-min-go, Paid no more at-ten-tion to

Bin-go. He went ver-y well · un - til he · fell · In
Bin-go? My coat is but yel - low, but still I'm a fel-low Whose
Bin-go. She stood with a smile on the bank of the Nile, · And

love with the fa - tal Fla - min-go. Fla - min-go, Fla - min-go, The
friends think him rath - er a Stin-go." Fla - min-go, Fla - min-go, She
thought, "By and by I will in go!" The Din-go, the Din-go, Re-

fa - tal - ly fair · Fla - min - go, No mate was · she, as you'll
scorn - ful - ly stared at Bin - go; And said, "Go a - way! I ·
pulsed by the cru - el Fla - min - go, Rushed in - to the wave to his

read - i - ly see, For the quad-ru-pe-dan-ti-cal Din-go.
can-not to-day Take the trou-ble to fol-low your lin - go!"
wa-ter - y grave, And · that was the end of poor Bin-go. (*omit repeat*)

Sailing

GODFREY MARKS

Con spirito
UNISON or BASS SOLO

1. Y'heave ho! · my lads, · the wind blows free; · A pleas - ant
2. The sail - or's life · is bold and free; · His home · is
3. The tide · is flow - ing with the gale; · Y'heave ho! · my

gale · is on our lee, · And soon · a-cross · the
on · the roll-ing sea; · And nev · er heart · more
lads, · set ev - 'ry sail, · The har - bor bar · we

o - cean clear · Our gal — lant bark · shall brave - ly
true or brave · Than he · who launch - es on · the
soon shall clear, · Fare-well · once more · to home · so

SOPRANO and ALTO
p

steer; · But ere we part · from Eng-land's shore to - night · A
wave. · A - far he speeds · in dis - tant lands to roam; · With
dear. · For when the tem - pest rag - es loud and long, · That

cres. poco a poco

song we'll sing · for home and beau - ty bright. ·
jo - cund song · he rides the spar - kling foam. ·
home shall be · our guid - ing stars a - mong.

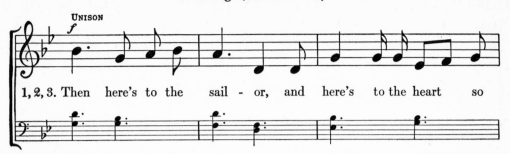

1, 2, 3. Then here's to the sail - or, and here's to the heart so

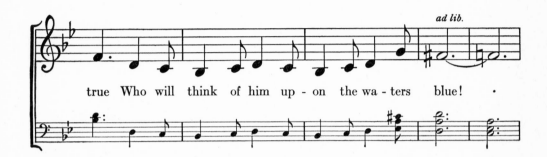

true Who will think of him up - on the wa - ters blue!

Sail - ing, sail - ing o - ver the bound - ing main; For

man - y a storm - y wind shall blow ere Jack comes home a -

gain. Sail-ing, sail-ing o - ver the bound-ing main; For

man - y a storm - y wind shall blow ere Jack comes home a - gain.

The Mysterious Ring

Adapted from an old tale

FRANCES McCOLLIN

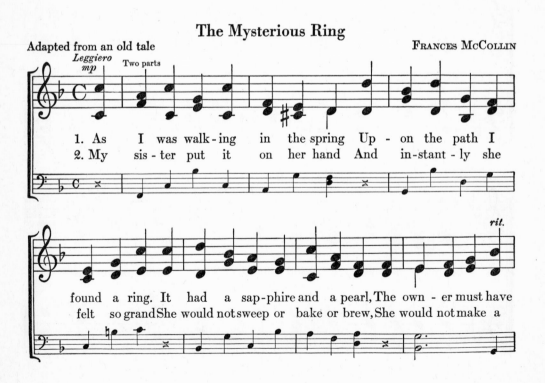

1. As I was walk-ing in the spring Up - on the path I
2. My sis - ter put it on her hand And in-stant-ly she

found a ring. It had a sap-phire and a pearl, The own - er must have
felt so grand She would not sweep or bake or brew, She would not make a

Wrap Me in Peace

DU BIST DIE RUH

Friedrich Rückert
Translated by Christine Turner Curtis

Franz Schubert

1. Set in my heart thy ra - diance mild.
2. Stay by my side, and bring me rest.

Wrap me in still - ness un - de - filed. Thy mood of
En - ter and make my heart thy nest. Ban - ish my

qui - et   on · me · im -   pose,   Save me   from tu - mult,
long - ing, ban - ish my · fear.   I lack   no bless - ing

grant me · re - pose,   · Grant · me · re - pose.   ·
when thou art · near,   · When · thou · art · near.   ·

3. Bless - ings   of

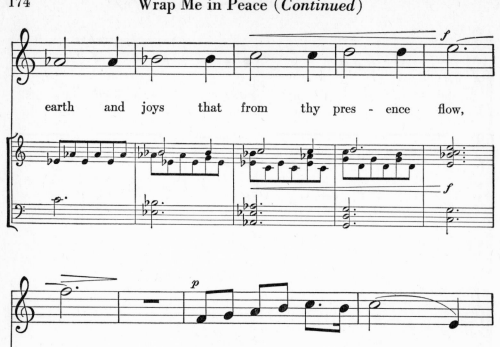

earth   and   joys   that   from   thy   pres - ence   flow,

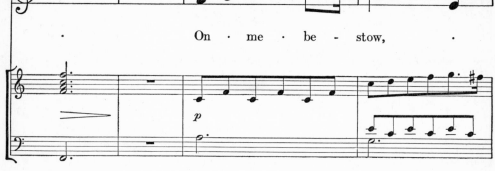

On · me · be - stow, ·

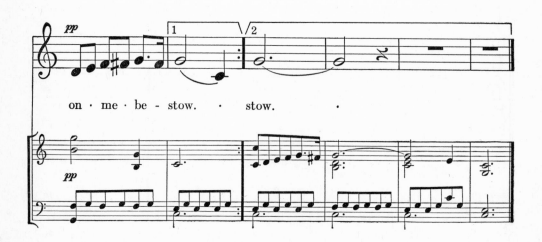

on · me · be - stow. · stow. ·

Dreams

FRENCH FOLK SONG
Arranged by FREDERICK A. TAYLOR

Translated from
the original

1. If I should chance to fall a-sleep On a la-zy sum-mer
2. If I should chance to fall a-sleep On a bed of ei-der

1. If I should chance to fall a-sleep On a sum - mer
2. If I should chance to fall a-sleep On a bed of

day, I'd dream a-bout a Har - le - quin
down, I'd dream I had a pa - per bag

day, I'd dream a - bout a Har - le - quin
down, I'd dream I had a pa - per bag

In a suit of red and gray. A thou - sand sil - ver
Full of al-monds, pale and brown. How faith - ful - ly my

Dressed in gray. A thou - sand
Al - monds brown. How faith - ful

bells would ring, Ding, din-gle doo, and doo-dle ding, As
friends would cling! Ting, tin-gle too, and too-dle ting, I'd

bells ring, Ding doo, doo-dle ding, As
friends cling! Ting too, too-dle ting, I'd

he be-gan to whirl and spring; Ding, din-gle doo-dle ding.
nev-er lack for an-y-thing. Ting, tin-gle too-dle ting.

he be-gan to whirl and spring; Ding, doo-dle ding.
nev-er lack for an-y-thing. Ting, too-dle ting.

When I Was a Lad

W. S. GILBERT

ARTHUR SULLIVAN
From "H.M.S. Pinafore"

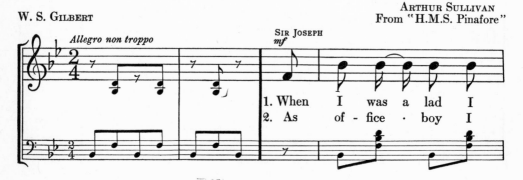

1. When I was a lad I
2. As of-fice boy I

pol - ished up the han - dle so · care - ful - lee That
cop - ied all the let - ters in a hand so free, And

CHORUS
f

now I am the rul - er of the Queen's Na - vee. He
now I am the rul - er of the Queen's Na - vee. He

pol - ished up that han - dle so · care - ful - lee That
cop - ied all the let - ters in a hand so free, And

now he is the rul - er of the Queen's Na - vee.
now he is the rul - er of the Queen's Na - vee.

O God, the Rock of Ages

Edward Bickersteth

Samuel Wesley

1. O God, the Rock of a - ges, Who ev - er - more hast been,
2. O Thou, Who canst not slum - ber, Whose light grows nev - er pale,

What time the tem - pest rag - es, Our dwell - ing place se - rene;
Teach us a - right to num - ber Our years be - fore they fail.

Be - fore Thy first cre - a - tions, O Lord, the same as now,
On us Thy mer - cy light - en, On us Thy good - ness rest;

To end - less gen - er - a - tions The ev - er - last - ing Thou.
And let Thy spir - it bright - en The hearts Thy - self hath blessed.

Lonely Shepherd

English version by
PIERSON UNDERWOOD

SLOVAK FOLK SONG
Arranged by LAWRENCE PERRY

1. "Faith - ful shep-herd, wait-ing morn-ing's pale beam, Night goes
2. "Turn, young shep-herd, on the jour - ney toward home! Cold winds

slow - ly, cold the mead-ow - lands seem!" "No, while light from one far
blow; your flock no long - er should roam!" "No, no! Near yon win-dow

win-dow shines on, Soon, too soon the mead-ows glim - mer with dawn!"
dream-ing I'll · stay. Dreams will van-ish with the dawn-ing of · day!"

Trail Song

HAROLD SYMMES

HENRY HADLEY

Then it's ho! · for the pack On the dust - y track, And
Breathe · deep · · their air So · clear and rare, Breathe

ho! for the road - side rills. A song for the trail Through
deep the · joy that thrills. Though mus - cles · ache, No

gorge · · and swale, That leads to the gi - ant hills.
steep · · for-sake; There's strength in the gi - ant hills.

Then up! Storm the heights Where first dawn lights, And
Then up, up and sing Till rock walls ring And

Then up! Storm the heights Where first dawn lights, And
Then up, up and sing Till rock walls ring And

Optional

vales where noth - ing stills The thun-der-ing call Of ·
ech - o heav-en fills! A wild · heigh-ho To the

vales where noth - ing stills The thun-der-ing call Of ·
ech - o heav-en fills! A wild · heigh-ho To the

cres.

stream and fall In the heart of the gi - ant hills.
vale be - low! Life · sings in the gi - ant hills.

stream and fall In the heart of the gi - ant hills.
vale be - low! Life · sings in the gi - ant hills.

The Meeting of the Waters

THOMAS MOORE

IRISH FOLK SONG

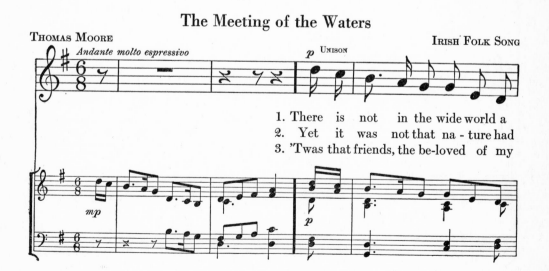

1. There is not in the wide world a
2. Yet it was not that na - ture had
3. 'Twas that friends, the be-loved of my

val - ley　so sweet　As that　vale　in　whose bos - om　the
shed o'er　the scene　Her ·　pur - est　of · crys - tal　and
bos - om,　were near,　Who made　ev - 'ry　dear　scene of　en -

cres.

bright wa - ters meet.　Oh! the　last rays　of · feel - ing　and
bright - est　of green;　'Twas ·　not　the　soft · mag - ic　of
chant - ment more dear;　And who　felt　how　the · best charms of

cres.

mf

life　must　de - part,　Ere the　bloom　of　that　val - ley shall
stream - let　or　hill;　Oh, ·　no　it　was　some - thing more
na - ture　im - prove　When we　see　them re - flect - ed　in

mf

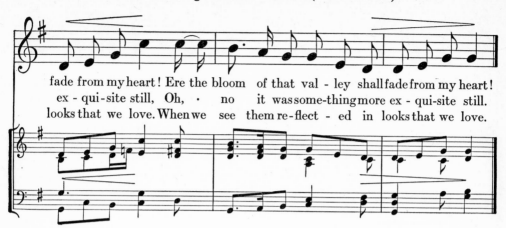

fade from my heart! Ere the bloom of that val - ley shall fade from my heart!
ex - qui-site still, Oh, · no it was some-thing more ex - qui-site still.
looks that we love. When we see them re-flect - ed in looks that we love.

Florian's Song

J. P. Claris de Florian
Translated

Benjamin Godard

1. If you should meet a shep-herd stray -
2. If with his lay the woods are ring -

ing With - in the vil - lage or the town,
ing, And all the ech - oes call his name,

8

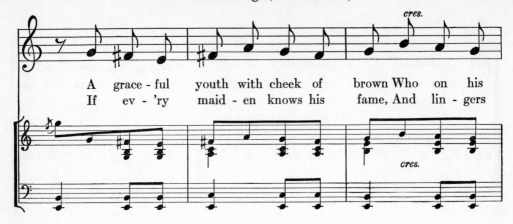

A grace - ful youth with cheek of brown Who on his
If ev - 'ry maid - en knows his fame, And lin - gers

pipe a tune is play - ing, He is the one

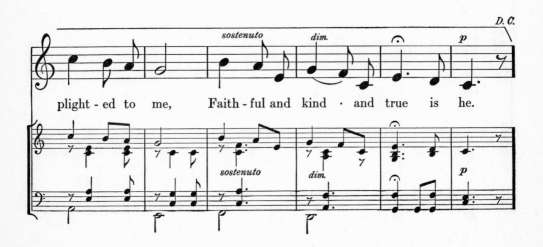

plight - ed to me, Faith - ful and kind · and true is he.

near to hear him sing - ing. He is the one plight-ed to

me, Faith - ful and kind · and true is he.

Daniel Boone

Pierson Underwood

Lawrence Perry

1. In the dark of woods where the brown deer run, And the
3. But he died at last in a house in bed, And his

leaf - green shad - ows cov - er the sun, In a time gone by, long
old fur cap was still on his head. You could hear the woods in

o - ver and done Like a haunt - ing tale or a tune: Was a
all that he said, And his eyes were bright as the moon; Like a

* This baritone solo may be sung in unison if preferred.

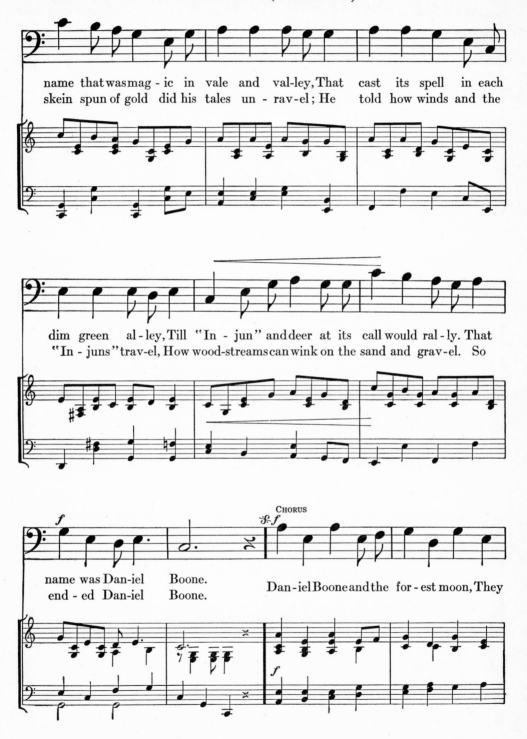

name that was mag - ic in vale and val - ley, That   cast   its   spell   in each
skein spun of gold did his tales un - rav - el; He   told   how winds and the

dim green   al - ley, Till "In - jun" and deer at its   call would ral - ly. That
"In - juns" trav - el, How wood-streams can wink on the sand and grav - el.   So

Chorus

name was Dan-iel   Boone.
end - ed Dan-iel   Boone.

Dan-iel Boone and the for - est moon, They

roamed in the dark to - geth - er; When nights are chill he

wan-ders still, To walk with wind and with weath - er. 2. When the

stars winked out in a night like pitch He could strike a blaze in

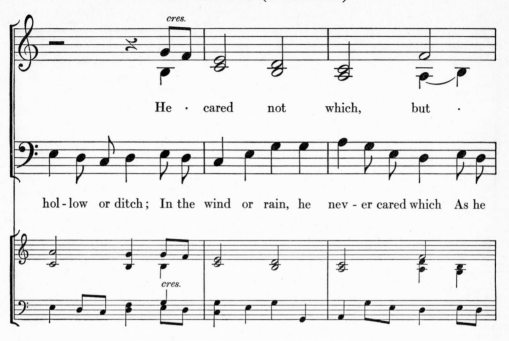

He · cared   not   which,   but   ·

hol-low or ditch; In the wind or rain, he   nev - er cared which As he

slept   to   its ·   croon. Though his buck-skins were worn   as   his

fell a - sleep to   its   croon.   Home   -   spun

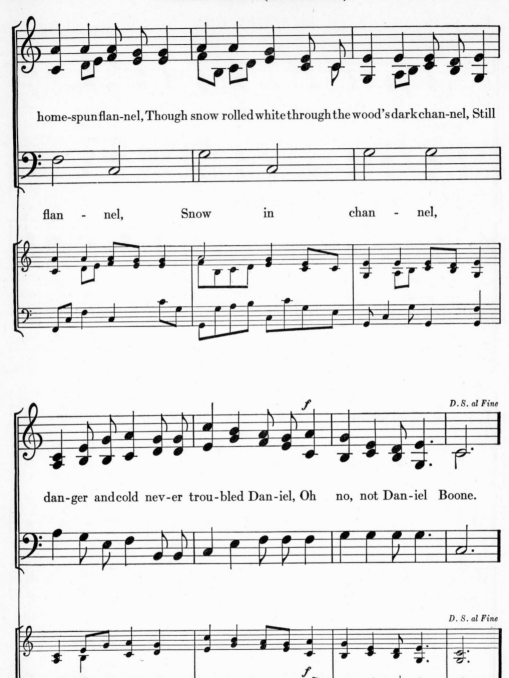

home-spun flan-nel, Though snow rolled white through the wood's dark chan-nel, Still

flan - nel,   Snow   in   chan - nel,

dan-ger and cold nev-er trou-bled Dan-iel, Oh   no, not Dan-iel Boone.

D. S. al Fine

My Old Kentucky Home[1]

RECREATION SONG

STEPHEN C. FOSTER

STEPHEN C. FOSTER

Andantino
mp

1. The sun shines bright in the old Ken-tuck-y home, 'Tis
2. They hunt no more for the pos-sum and the coon, On
3. The head must bow and the back will have to bend, Wher-

sum-mer, the dark-ies are gay; The corn-top's ripe and the
mead-ow, the hill and the shore; They sing no more by the
ev-er the dark-y may go; A few more days and the

mead-ow's in the bloom, While the birds make mu-sic all the
glim-mer of the moon, On the bench by the old cab-in
trou-ble all will end, In the field where the sug-ar canes

day. The young folk roll on the lit-tle cab-in floor, All
door. The day goes by like a shad-ow o'er the heart, With
grow. A few more days for to tote the wea-ry load, No

[1] This song may be sung in unison if desired.

mer - ry, all hap - py and bright; By'n by hard times come a -
sor - row where all was de - light; The time has come when the
mat - ter, 'twill nev - er be light; A few more days till we

knock - ing at the door, Then my old Ken-tuck - y home, good -
dark - ies have to part, Then my old Ken-tuck - y home, good -
tot - ter on the road, Then my old Ken-tuck - y home, good -

CHORUS

night!
night! 1, 2, 3. Weep no more, my la - dy, Oh,
night!

weep no more to - day! We will sing one song for the

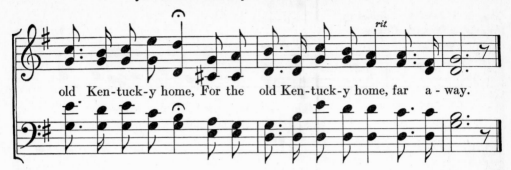

old Ken-tuck-y home, For the old Ken-tuck-y home, far a-way.

Ring, Ring the Banjo

RECREATION SONG

STEPHEN C. FOSTER

STEPHEN C. FOSTER

Moderato
mf

1. The time is nev-er drear-y If the dark-y nev-er groans; The
2. Oh, nev-er count the bub-bles While there's wa-ter in the spring. The

la-dies nev-er wea-ry With the rat-tle of the bones.
dark-y has no trou-bles While he's got this song to sing.

(CHORUS) Come a-gain my true love; Oh, · where you been so long,

CHORUS

Ring, ring the ban-jo! I like that good old song;

O Marie

Translated from the original by
CHRISTINE TURNER CURTIS

E. DI CAPUA

1. Un - der your leaf - y win - dow, ·
2. See · in her loft - y win - dow, ·

Pa - tient I stand and wait. · · Send · me a kind-ly mes - sage,
Lamp - light has made a star. · · Loud - er, and more im-plor - ing

Tell · me my fu - ture fate. · Morn - ing and noon and
Ring, · ring, my sweet gui - tar. · Tell · of my love and

eve - ning, · No · res-pite have I known, ·
long - ing, · Swear · I'll be al - ways true. ·

Hop - ing to hear your an - swer, Sing - ing for you a -
Say · that with-out her near me, Pleas - ures are far and

lone.
few.

Alto optional
mf

1, 2. O Ma - rie, · O Ma - rie, · you're the sun and plan-ets to

mf

O Marie (*Continued*)

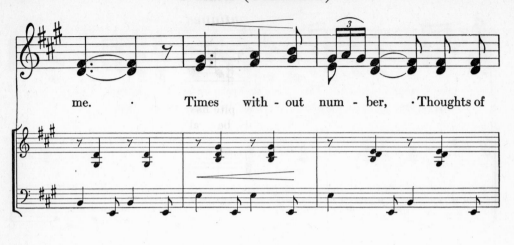

me. Times with - out num - ber, Thoughts of

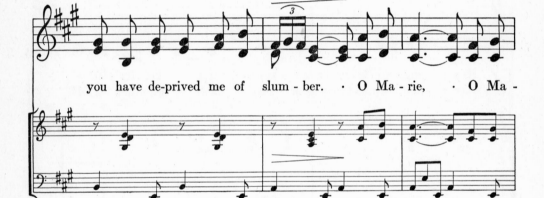

you have de-prived me of slum - ber. O Ma - rie, O Ma -

cres.

rie, you're the stars and the moon-beams to me.

Hark to my plea, · · O Ma-rie, · O Ma-rie. ·

I Sho' Am Glad

VICTOR YOUNG   VICTOR YOUNG

I sho' am glad I'se liv-in': I'se

thank-ful as can be For all duh things dat Prov-i-dence has

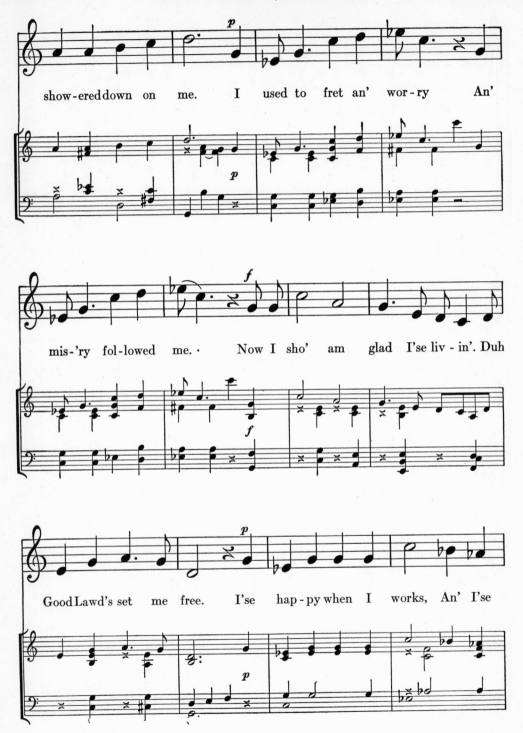

show-ered down on me.   I   used to fret an' wor-ry   An'

mis-'ry fol-lowed me. ·   Now I sho'   am   glad I'se liv-in'. Duh

Good Lawd's set   me free.   I'se   hap-py when I   works,   An' I'se

hap - py when I sits, An' mah heart jes' o - ver - flows For duh

peace o' mind I gits.   Dat ole hon - ey - suck - le's sweet - er, An' a

rob - in in de tree Chirps out Hal - le - lu - jah like In his

song jes' writ fo'   me.   ·   I sho' am

glad I'se liv - in', I'se thank-ful as   can   be   For all duh things dat

Prov - i - dence Has show-ered down on me.

Dixie

Dan D. Emmett

RECREATION SONG

Dan D. Emmett

1. I · wish I was · in the
2. There buck-wheat cakes and ·

land of cot - ton, Old times there are not for-got-ten, Look a -
In - dian bat - ter Make you fat or a lit - tle fat-ter, Look a -

way! Look a - way! Look a - way! Dix - ie Land! In ·
way! Look a - way! Look a - way! Dix - ie Land! Then

Dix - ie Land where I was born · · Ear - ly on one
hoe it down and · scratch your grav-el, to Dix - ie Land I'm

frost - y morn, · Look a - way! Look a - way! Look a -
bound to trav - el, Look a - way! Look a - way! Look a -

way! Dix - ie Land!
way! Dix - ie Land! Then I wish I was in

Dix - ie, Hoo - ray! Hoo - ray! In Dix - ie Land I'll

take my stand To live and die in Dix - ie, A -

way, (a - way) a - way, (a - way) A - way down South in Dix - ie, A -

[1] Parts are optional.

way, (a - way) a - way, (a - way) A - way down South in Dix - ie.

Hail, Poetry

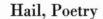

W. S. GILBERT

ARTHUR SULLIVAN

From "The Pirates of Penzance"

Hail, po - e - try, thou heav'n-born maid! Thou gild - est

e'en the Pi - rate's trade. Hail, flow-ing fount of sen - ti -

ment, all hail! All hail! di - vine e - mol - li - ent.

The Minstrel

Adapted by
CECIL COWDREY

OLD WELSH MELODY

Allegretto mp

1. At dawn of day I roamed the wood Where dew - y boughs were
2. O black - bird, sing thy cheer - ful song, With - out a note of

1. At dawn of day I roamed the wood Where dew - y boughs were
2. O black - bird, sing thy cheer - ful song, With - out a note of

Optional

swing - ing, A - mid the blos - soms crowd - ed close I
sad - ness; For thee the sum - mer's gold - en hours Can

swing - ing, A - mid the blos - soms crowd - ed close I
sad - ness; For thee the sum - mer's gold - en hours Can

heard a · black - bird sing - ing. And as I stood in
ech - o - on - ly glad - ness. But ev - 'ry min - strel's

heard a black - bird sing - ing. And as I stood in
ech - o on - ly glad - ness. But ev - 'ry min - strel's

joy - ous mood My harp to si - lence hush - ing, His
harp o - beys His mood though dark or lone - ly, While

joy - ous mood My harp to si - lence hush - ing, His
harp o - beys His mood though dark or lone - ly, While

mer - ry song came float - ing down, My cheeks with pleas - ure flush-ing.
still thy feath - ered throat shall yield But joy - ful meas - ures on - ly.

mer - ry song came float - ing down, My cheeks with pleas - ure flush - ing.
still thy feath - ered throat shall yield But joy - ful meas - ures on - ly.

Oh! Susanna

STEPHEN C. FOSTER   RECREATION SONG   STEPHEN C. FOSTER

1. I · came from Al - a -
2. I · had a dream the
3. I · soon will be in

Oh! Susanna (*Continued*)

ba - ma, With my ban - jo on my knee, I'm
oth - er night When ev - 'ry-thing was still, I ·
New Or - leans, And then I'll look a - round, And

gwine to Lou' - si - an - a My · true love for to see; It ·
thought I saw Su - san-na A - com-ing down the hill; The
when I find Su - san-na I will fall up - on the ground, And

rained all night the day I left, The weath-er it was dry, The
buck-wheat cake was in her mouth, The tear was in her eye; Says
if I do not find · her, This dark-y'll sure-ly cry. And

sun so hot I froze to death, Su - san-na, don't you cry.
I, "I'm com - ing from the South, Su - san-na, don't you cry."
when I'm dead and bur - ied, Su - san-na, don't you cry.

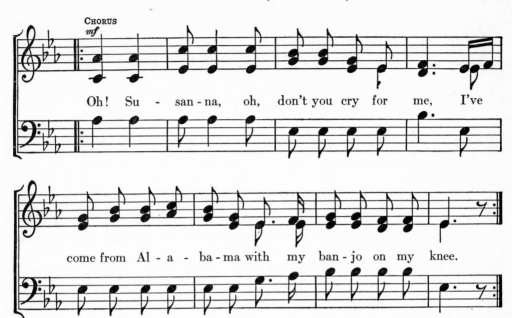

Oh! Su - san - na, oh, don't you cry for me, I've

come from Al - a - ba - ma with my ban - jo on my knee.

The Midshipmite

FRED E. WEATHERLY

STEPHEN ADAMS

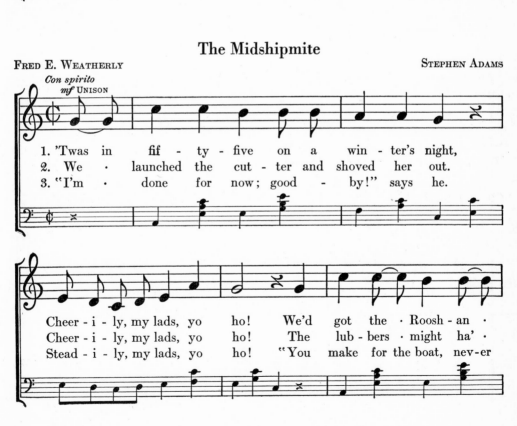

Con spirito
mf UNISON

1. 'Twas in fif - ty - five on a win - ter's night,
2. We · launched the cut - ter and shoved her out.
3. "I'm · done for now; good - by!" says he.

Cheer - i - ly, my lads, yo ho! We'd got the · Roosh - an ·
Cheer - i - ly, my lads, yo ho! The lub - bers · might ha' ·
Stead - i - ly, my lads, yo ho! "You make for the boat, nev - er

lines   in   sight   When ·   up   comes   a   lit - tle ·
heard   us   shout   As the   Mid - dy ·   cried, "Now, my
mind   for   me!" "We'll ·   take   'ee ·   back   or ·

Parts optional

Mid - ship-mite.   Cheer - i - ly, my lads, yo   ho!   "Who'll ·
lads, put   a - bout."   Cheer - i - ly, my lads, yo   ho!   We ·
die," ·   says we.   Cheer - i - ly, my lads, yo   ho!   So we

go   a - shore   to - night," ·   says   he,   "An' ·
made   for   the guns   an' ·   rammed ·   'em   tight,   But   the
hoist - ed   him   in   in ·   ter - ri - ble   plight,   An'   we

UNISON
f

spike   their · guns   a - long wi' me?" "Why, bless 'ee, ·   sir, come a-
mus - ket · shots came   left and right,   An' down drops the poor lit - tle
pulled,   ev-'ry man with   all   his might,   An' saved the ·   poor lit - tle

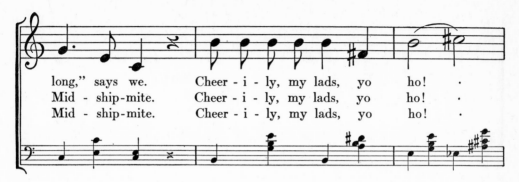

long," says we.   Cheer - i - ly, my lads, yo ho!   ·
Mid - ship-mite.   Cheer - i - ly, my lads, yo ho!   ·
Mid - ship-mite.   Cheer - i - ly, my lads, yo ho!   ·

1,2,3. Cheer - i - ly, my lads, yo ho!   · With a long, long

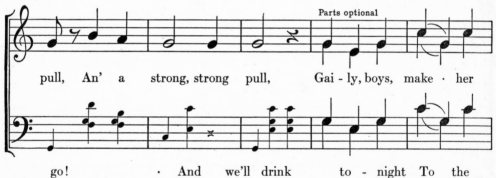

pull, An' a strong, strong pull,   Gai - ly, boys, make · her

go!   · And we'll drink to - night To the

(make her) go!   Drink to - night,

Mid - ship - mite, Sing - ing cheer - i - ly, lads, yo ho!

The Serenaders

Pierson Underwood

Italian Folk Tune
Arranged by Lawrence Perry

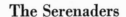

1. Bright the · moon, soft the tune that our strings are
2. Yet, be - ware! Bright the air where our songs are

send - ing Through the night, with the light breez - es blend - ing.
ring - ing! Par - ents stern soon may learn who comes sing - ing.

Here or there, maid - ens fair, from their win - dows bend - ing,
Is it wrong, with a song, while the night is wing - ing,

Tenor and Bass

Lean to hear some-one near as he plays his gui - tar.
'Neath each bright win-dow's light just to play the gui - tar?

Chorus
Four part

A - bove the strum - ming, soft voic - es hum - ming,

Set puls-es drum-ming near and far. Each cav - a - lier, now,

shall have no fear, now, To ser-e - nade with his gui - tar.

The Old Chisholm[1] Trail[2]

RECREATION SONG

TRADITIONAL

COWBOY SONG

Moderato
mp

1. Come a-long, boys, · and · lis-ten to my tale; I'll
2. Start-ed my trail · Oc - to-ber twen-ty-third, I
3. Woke up one morn-ing on the Old · Chis-holm Trail, A

tell you all my trou-bles on the Old Chis-holm Trail.
start-ed up the trail · with the Two U · herd.
rope · in my right hand and a cow by the tail.

REFRAIN

Come a ti yi you - py, you - py

[1] Pronounced "chiz-zum."　　　[2] This song may be sung in unison if desired.

yah, you-py yah! Come a ti yi you-py, you-py yah!

4. It's bacon and beans most every day;
   I'd as soon be eating prairie hay.

5. Went to the boss to draw my roll;
   He had me figured out nine dollars in the hole.

6. I'll sell my outfit as soon as I can,
   And I won't punch cattle for any man.

7. With my knees in the saddle and my seat in the sky,
   I'll quit punching cows in the sweet by and by.

Flemish Bells[1]

Translated from the original by
JOHN SUMNER

FLEMISH FOLK SONG

1. A - cross the fields and down the lanes, From loft - y Flem-ish
2. Where wind-mills lift their la - zy sails Be-neath the low-land

[1] This song may be sung in unison if desired.

tow'rs,   The   mu - sic   of   a   thou - sand bells   Rings
skies,   The   rip - pling riv - er   slips   and sings,   And

out   the   day - light · hours.   A - long   the   riv - ers ·
with   the   bel - fry · vies;   But   voic - es   rich   and ·

wide   and deep, Where   pleas - ant pas - tures   lie   a - sleep,
sil - ver clear Clang   from   on   high   for · all   to   hear.

Ring clear from   an - cient bel - fries, Flem - ish bells, chim - ing bells.
Ring clear from   an - cient bel - fries, Flem - ish bells, chim - ing bells.

O Tennessee!

Louise Stickney

Septimus Winner

Second part optional

1. O Ten - nes-see, old Ten - nes-see, my home of long a-
2. O Ten - nes-see, O Ten - nes-see, your or-chards bloom and -

go,   Where riv - ers down their peace - ful way Are -
shine, The red - bird nods a sau - cy crest, And the

flow - ing wide and · slow.   So   car - ry me back to
mock - er sings like · nine.

REFRAIN
Parts optional

Ten - nes - see,   There all the good things meet, Where

8

The Star-Spangled Banner

FRANCIS SCOTT KEY

JOHN STAFFORD SMITH

1. Oh, · say, can you see, · by the dawn's ear - ly light, What so proud - ly we
2. Oh, · thus be it ev - er when · free - men shall stand Be - tween their loved

hailed at the twi-light's last gleam - ing, Whose broad stripes and bright stars, through the
homes and the war's des - o - la - tion! Blest with vic - t'ry and peace, may the

per - il - ous fight, O'er the ram - parts we watched were so gal - lant - ly
heav'n - res - cued land Praise the Pow'r that hath made and pre-served us a

stream - ing? And the rock-et's red glare, the bombs burst - ing in air, Gave
na - tion! Then con-quer we must, when our cause it is just, And

proof through the night that our flag was still there. Oh, · say, does that star-span - gled
this be our mot-to: "In · God is our trust!" And the star-span-gled ban - ner in

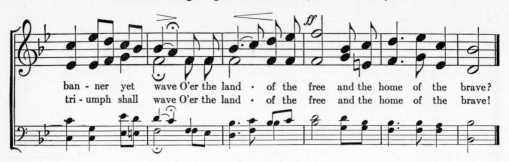

ban - ner yet wave O'er the land · of the free and the home of the brave?
tri - umph shall wave O'er the land · of the free and the home of the brave!

America

SAMUEL F. SMITH   HENRY CAREY

1. My coun - try! 'tis of thee, Sweet land of lib - er - ty,
2. My na - tive coun - try, thee, — Land of the no - ble free, —
3. Let mu - sic swell the breeze, And ring from all the trees
4. Our fa - thers' God! to Thee, Au - thor of lib - er - ty,

Of thee I sing; Land where my fa - thers died! Land of the
Thy name I love; I love thy rocks and rills, Thy woods and
Sweet free-dom's song; Let mor - tal tongues a - wake, Let all that
To Thee we sing; Long may our land be bright With free-dom's

Pil - grims' pride! From ev - 'ry · moun-tain side Let · free-dom ring.
tem - pled hills; My heart with rap - ture thrills Like · that a - bove.
breathe par - take, Let rocks their si - lence break, The · sound pro - long.
ho - ly light! Pro - tect · us · by Thy might, Great God, our King!

Alphabetical Index

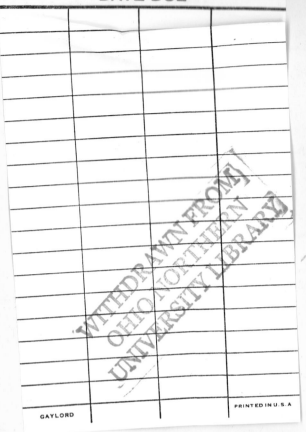